Frank Pierce Jones

FREEDOM TO CHANGE

GW00566710

F. Matthias Alexander (1869–1955)

Frank Pierce Jones

FREEDOM TO CHANGE

The Development and Science of
The Alexander Technique

Introduction by J. McVicker Hunt
Foreword by Ted Dimon

MOURITZ

First published 1976 as
Body Awareness in Action
by Schocken Books, New York
Second edition 1979

Third edition published May 1997 by

Mouritz Ltd.
6 Ravenslea Road
London SW12 8SB
United Kingdom

Reprinted March 2003

Appendix E edited by Jean M. O. Fischer
Glossary and selected bibliography
prepared by Richard A. Brown
© 1997 The Estate of Frank Pierce Jones

ISBN 0–9525574–7–9 Paperback

A CIP Catalogue record for this book
is available from the British Library

Cover design, layout and
typesetting by Jean M. O. Fischer
Printed on 90 gsm High Opaque
and bound in Great Britain by
Bookcraft, Midsomer Norton, Bath

Contents

The colour plates (I-IV) are inserted between p. 110 and p. 111.

Introduction

THIS BOOK OFFERS a variety of things seldom attempted in a single work, but here they are combined naturally and successfully. In it, Frank Jones takes his readers from an autobiographical, subjective account of his experience with the Alexander Technique to an objective, data-based theory of the mechanism which accounts for the subjective sense of kinaesthetic lightness that is its hallmark. Along the way, Jones describes what led the originator to develop the Technique and how he did it. He synopsizes the successive works that the originator, F. Matthias Alexander, wrote and the impressions that they, along with the experience of the Technique, made on such illustrious figures as Dr. George Ellett Coghill, Sir Stafford Cripps, John Dewey, Aldous Huxley, James Harvey Robinson, Bernard Shaw and Sir Charles Sherrington. A chapter with detective-story quality on the successful court action brought in South Africa by F. M. Alexander against the editors of *Manpower* for an article accusing him of false claims introduces the need for research showing "at least the physical equivalents of the great mental experience" of kinaesthetic lightness. The major contribution of the book is Jones's description of his methods, which he derived from experimental psychology, and the results of his research. Jones's results go a long way toward fulfilling this need for the physical equivalents. Finally, he synthesizes the results from his own research with knowledge of anatomy, mechanics and physiology to create a testable theory of the mechanism, and presents his views of the teaching process. It is a marvellous literary and scientific achievement for a lifetime, but it all came in the latter half of Jones's life. At age 33, he was still a classical scholar teaching Greek at Brown University. Before his untimely death, Jones considered *Freedom to Change* as the title of this work. By this "freedom," he referred to what must be learned in the Technique to permit one to change deliberately one's use of oneself, but his life and his work are a splendid example of an extension of such a limited semantic reference.

The Technique was developed by F. Matthias Alexander, who was giving one-man recitations from Shakespeare and other authors in the 1890s. When hoarseness and loss of voice that rest and medical aid would not cure incapacitated him, Alexander decided that something he was doing to himself while reciting must be causing the trouble. With a special arrangement of mirrors, he came to see that whenever he began to recite he rotated his head "backward and down" and so depressed his larynx that he was forced to breathe in audible gasps. He learned gradually that he could consciously inhibit this stressful pattern. Once he had learned this, he found that he could initiate new activity toward any end or goal he might choose. Achieving this inhibition called for concentration on what he termed the "means-whereby principle" to avoid reversion to the stressful habitual pattern in seeking to achieve the end he had in view. Thus, "end-gaining" became a bad word. When he could resume his reciting without a return of the hoarseness, he shared his experience. This led others to seek help with similar vocal problems from him and his brother, A. R. Alexander, who joined him in what they came to call "the work." Gradually they developed a way of teaching the Technique that prompted a prominent surgeon in Sydney to send the brothers to London with letters of introduction to actors and physicians in order to provide them with a wider and more influential audience.

F. M. Alexander soon began writing, first pamphlets and then books, about the Technique, but it has always been difficult to characterize and describe in words. His effort to communicate the means of inhibiting habitual and damaging use of the body in order to achieve this kinaesthetic lightness in action led, as is always the case with new domains of concern and investigation, to special terminology. The result was instructions containing such terms as "concentrate on the 'means whereby' rather than 'end-gaining'," "think of the head as 'forward and up' but do not actively thrust it forward or up," and such theoretical constructions as "position of mechanical advantage," "primary control" and "faulty sensory appreciation."

Although such words by themselves failed to communicate, the Alexanders could quickly use their hands to induce in nearly anyone who would expose himself to a "lesson" a relationship among head, neck, shoulders and back that induced a dramatic impression of kinaesthetic lightness in action. So long as one retained this new postural relationship ("primary control"), one could readily carry out common actions without the accustomed sense of effort and strain. This impression of kinaesthetic lightness from a single demonstration persists, at least for a short time, and memory of it lingers for life. Moreover, once an individual had learned to achieve the new postural relationship ("primary control") of the Alexander Technique on his own initiative, stress-produced problems such as, for example, Alexander's hoarseness, disappear. Although few physicians have ever become attracted to the Technique for therapeutic purposes, Dr. Wilfred Barlow and a few others have reported finding it useful in such varied conditions as "peptic ulcer, spastic colon, ulcerated colitis, eczema and rheumatoid arthritis" as well as "tension headaches, asthma, low-back pain and fibrositis."

Although F. M. Alexander wrote in captivating fashion about the Technique, his words as such seldom elicited faith in its efficacy and validity. It was undoubtedly demonstrations of the dramatic experience of kinaesthetic lightness coupled with relief from distressful symptoms of misuse in those who learned through lessons to achieve "primary control" voluntarily, that convinced such figures as Sir Stafford Cripps, John Dewey, Aldous Huxley, James Harvey Robinson and Bernard Shaw of its validity. Aldous Huxley introduced F. M. Alexander as the character of Miller, a redemptive figure in the guise of a medical anthropologist, who showed the hero of his novel, *Eyeless in Gaza*, how to change. Huxley gave the Technique a more formal endorsement in *Ends and Means*. Huxley was a pupil who came back repeatedly whenever distressful symptoms convinced him that his use of himself had again become habitually wrong in some fashion. John Dewey was one of Alexander's earliest American pupils. In 1918, he wrote an introduction to a new American edition of Alexander's book entitled *Man's Supreme Inheritance*. Dewey considered that the Alexander Technique provided a demonstration of the unity of body and mind. With progress as a pupil, he reported an improvement in his vision and in his breathing and in ability to hold a philosophical position calmly with ability to change it if new evidence warranted.

In his *Experience and Nature*, Dewey acknowledges the influence of Alexander on his view of habit as given in the chapter entitled "Nature, life and body-mind." Dewey's conception of habit and Alexander's conception of "faulty sensory appreciation" may be seen to resemble Harry Helson's more recently-formulated concept of the "adaptation level." Herein is a domain of tremendous motivational significance that deserves more investigation and is beginning to receive it.

"Going to Alexander" became quite fashionable in intellectual circles of England and America during the 1920s and the 1930s. Praise for the Technique from those who exposed themselves to it and became pupils was the rule. Those who merely heard or read about it, on the other hand, were prone to lump it among "faddish cures." They were also prone to attribute any long-term effects to the charisma of the Alexanders or to some such factor as suggestion. Although both of the Alexander brothers have been dead for a decade and a half, encomia for the Technique from men of intellectual fame persist. On 12 December 1973, Nikolaas Tinbergen, when he shared he Nobel Prize for Physiology and Medicine with Konrad Lorenz and Karl von Frisch, devoted half of his lecture of acceptance, delivered in Stockholm, to an account of the Alexander Technique. He referred to it as his "second example of the usefulness of an ethological approach to medicine." Tinbergen, his wife, and one of their daughters went to Alexander teachers, each to a different one. As they acquired proficiency in self-initiated achievement of "primary control" that brought the sense of kinaesthetic lightness, all noted, and with growing amazement, "very striking improvements in such diverse things as high blood-pressure, breathing, depth of sleep, overall cheerfulness and mental alertness, resilience against outside pressures, and in such a refined skill as playing a stringed instrument. So from personal experience we can already confirm some of the amazingly fantastic claims made by Alexander and his followers, namely, that many types of under-performance and even ailments, both mental and physical, can be alleviated, sometimes to a surprising extent, by teaching the body musculature to function differently" (Tinbergen, *Science*, 5 July 1974, 185 [4145] p. 25). Since both of the Alexander brothers had been dead a decade before the Tinbergens began their "lessons," their report rules out the charisma of the Alexanders as a basis for such effects of learning the Technique.

People, famous or not, are almost always motivated to consider becoming pupils of Alexander teachers by a hope of escaping some of their distressful symptoms. Sometime in 1938, such was Frank Jones's motivation for becoming a pupil of A. R. Alexander in Boston, for he was continually plagued by fatigue and muscular aches that came especially when he was sitting at his desk to read or write. I first heard of the Technique when Robert D. Scott, professor of English at the University of Nebraska, described his experience with it at a psychological colloquium in 1930. The basis of my own subsequent firsthand acquaintance with the Technique and, ultimately, with the Alexander brothers, was indirectly based on such a hope. Following the birth of our first child in 1933, my wife, Esther, developed a severely painful back. Frank Jones, Harold Schlosberg and I were then all members of the faculty of Brown University. We were also family friends. Harold Schlosberg, a fellow psychologist and collaborator of mine, suffered from severe arthritis. This motivated him to accept Frank Jones's suggestion that he become a pupil of A. R. Alexander. One night when we were all at the Schlosbergs, Esther decided to accept an invitation to accompany Frank and Harold to Boston for lessons with A. R. Alexander. Occasionally I went along. On several occasions, A. R. provided me with demonstrations of that dramatic feeling of kinaesthetic lightness. I also had a lesson or two, and met those participating in the Alexander training course for teachers of the Technique. On at least one of those visits, I also met F. M. Alexander. In the ensuing years, Esther has often referred to the Technique "as a way of lifting me up and out of myself whenever I find I am doing something painful to myself." She considers what she learned in those lessons with A. R. to have been her "saving stand-by through the years." The gains that Frank Jones experienced motivated him to take a leave of absence from his post at Brown University and to undertake the 3-year course required to qualify as an Alexander teacher. After A. R. returned to England in 1945, moreover, Harold Schlosberg continued as a pupil of Frank Jones.

As a teacher of the Alexander Technique, Frank Jones soon felt a need to establish it scientifically, a need to uncover "the physical equivalents of the great mental experience," and to discover a mechanism that would account for the long-term effects on health and well-being. Dewey had long recognized this need for objective evidence of the mechanism. Yet, despite F. M. Alexander's disappointing failure to share or even acknowledge such a need, Dewey nevertheless staked his reputation on his claim that "Mr. Alexander's technique is scientific in the strictest sense of the word."

Once he had established himself as a skilled teacher of the Technique, Frank Jones's desire for a more solid scientific foundation for it became a ruling concern. The first support for his research came as gifts from pupils whose recoveries from distressful symptoms motivated their generosity. He had to by-pass the obstacle of prejudiced prejudgement by established authorities at both Harvard and Massachusetts General Hospital before finding a place for his research. This he achieved through the hospitality of the Institute for Applied Experimental Psychology at Tufts University. There he chose to get comparative reports of felt effort associated with habitual postures and movements and with those that can be teacher-induced in a single lesson and then to investigate the anatomical and physiological correlates of the reported kinaesthetic lightness. He chose this approach rather than that of measuring changes in performance, appearance and personality that take place over a period of time following many lessons. He derived his research strategy and most of his instruments from experimental psychology. Such instruments included comparative psychophysical reports, multiple-image photography, electromyography and the strain-gauge force-platform. He also employed X-ray photography from medicine.

Jones started his investigation with the act of straightening up from a slump while sitting and while standing. This is the movement with which Dewey introduced his discussion of habit in his book entitled *Human Nature and Conduct*. When Jones requested psychophysical reports comparing the amounts of effort associated with the "habitual relaxed" and the "habitual erect" posture, all his pupil-subjects reported a marked increase associated with the latter. But when he requested comparisons of felt effort for the "habitual relaxed posture" and the "teacher-induced erect posture," they reported either "no increase" or an actual "decrease" of effort. By means of multiple-image photography which used a strobolume that flashed at differing rates, he measured differences between the "habitual" and "teacher-guided" patterns of movement. Those guided proved to be smoother and more regular and to contain more space than those habitual. By means of electromyography, he measured the changes in electrical potential associated with changes from "habitual erect postures" and found marked increases, but these increases failed to appear when the movement was "teacher guided." By means of X-ray photography, he could also differentiate the teacher-guided shift from relaxed to erect posture from the habitual self-directed form of this shift. Jones also found that when subjects shifted from their habitual relaxed to their habitual erect posture, their eye level remained virtually constant, but when they were guided into the erect posture by a teacher of the Alexander Technique, eye level dropped even though their sitting height increased.

Convenience for measurement dictated for study the choice of these postural shifts in sitting and standing in Jones's early experiments even though it is in movement rather than posture that the Alexander Technique is subjectively most obvious. When these methods employed with the postural shift were adapted for study of the movement from sitting to standing, even more striking differences in a number of indices were found between the habitual and the teacher-guided movements. When a strain-gauge force-platform was employed to measure directly the differences between the force exerted by the subject in such habitual and teacher-guided movements as that from sitting to standing, that for beginning to walk, and that for climbing stairs, the measurements indicated that teacher-guidance served to subtract an average of approximately 25 pounds of the force that the subjects typically used to start such movements. Such experiments, and there were others, clearly show an objective, organismic basis for the impression of kinaesthetic lightness almost universally reported by individuals who try a lesson.

Jones has combined these findings from his own research with what he has been able to learn about the mechanics of bones, ligaments and muscle, and about stretch reflexes, the centre of gravity for the head, and the process of inhibition, to formulate a theory of the long-term effects of learning how to achieve "primary control" voluntarily. The main substance of the theory is expressed in three hypotheses to be found on page 151. The name of Frank Pierce Jones must now rank right along with that of the originator in the establishment of the Alexander Technique.

When Frank Jones wrote to invite me to write an introduction to his book, I was delighted. Despite my pleasure in his invitation, the press of other obligations made me somewhat slow to respond. When I did answer, he was in the hospital. I wish I might have had his comments on these introductory remarks, but his death has deprived me of them. Others must carry on without his guidance. It was with considerable evidence of satisfaction that he wrote in his last letter to me that future teaching and research on the Alexander Technique would be in good hands. It is important for the health and welfare of many that this be so.

J. McVICKER HUNT
University of Illinois
March, 1976

Foreword to New Edition

SINCE THE PUBLICATION of this book in 1976 under the title of *Body Awareness in Action*, the name of Frank Pierce Jones has come to be regarded as synonymous with the Alexander Technique. Spanning more than three decades, Jones published over thirty papers on the Technique, corresponded with scientists, doctors, teachers, and students all over the world, and produced what many people feel is the finest writing on the subject. Published here under its original intended title, this book was written both as an introduction to the Technique and as a summary of Jones's extensive research into the subject. It has today become a classic, and it is one of the few books on the Technique regarded, not simply as an exposition of the Technique, but a substantive contribution to the field.

In the twenty-odd years that have followed the publication of this book, interest in Jones's work never diminished, and his wife, Helen, continued to answer requests from around the world about her husband's research and about the Technique. In response to this demand, Helen formed the Alexander Technique Archives (ATA) in 1982, a non-profit organization whose purpose would be to respond to requests about Jones's work and the Technique, to support scholarship and research on the Alexander Technique, and to form a repository of scholarly and historical material for future research. This material, which is now overseen by the ATA Board of Directors, has been given on permanent loan to the Tufts University Special Collections, and has been visited by scholars and students from around the world. It was also Helen's wish to publish all her husband's research papers—many of which had never been published before—in one volume, and thus to make Jones's research widely available to an audience that was unaware of its scope.

Helen's wish to see all her husband's work in print has at last come to fruition. In conjunction with SUNY Press, ATA is about to publish Jones's collected papers under the title *Mind and Motion: A Scientific Study of the Alexander Technique*, edited by Missy Vineyard; and this edition of *Freedom to Change* contains Jones's draft for a fifteenth chapter and a selection of his notes on the Technique.

These publications of Jones's work on the Alexander Technique come at a time when a growing appreciation of the need for new approaches to health has prompted a resurgence of interest in the Technique. Increasing numbers of people around the world are having lessons in the Technique, and introductory books on the subject abound. But this growth of interest in the Technique is not the same as an appreciation of Alexander's discoveries and of their significance in the fields of education and health. Awareness of the importance of Alexander's discovery of a "primary control" of the working of the musculoskeletal system, of the "use of the self" in all activities and its importance to health and functioning, and of Alexander's insistence on the indivisibility of mind and body—all these concepts are still unfamiliar to many people, and the far-reaching implications of Alexander's work are yet to be fully appreciated.

All the more reason, then, that Jones's writings be reprinted, for Jones's work doesn't simply promote the Technique, nor simply provide an introduction to the Technique (though it does these incomparably well); it elucidates the essential discoveries and insights on which the Alexander Technique is based. As such, this book, far from being just another good introduction to the Technique, is a crucial addition to the literature on the subject. It is also a summary of the many years of brilliant work Jones did in the field, a record of his essential insights, and a model for what remains to be done.

TED DIMON
President, Alexander Technique Archives, Inc.
Massachusetts
Februrary, 1997

Acknowledgments

I WISH TO EXPRESS my deepest gratitude to all who gave encouragement and assistance to my husband while he was writing this book. Many colleagues, students and friends read each chapter as soon as it was written and offered suggestions and criticism. When my husband died, the last chapter had been completed.

I am greatly indebted to Dr. John A. Hanson, Dr. Richard A. Brown and Dr. Donald L. Mixon for their careful reading of the entire manuscript and for their painstaking work in preparing it for publication, in assembling the photographs and in proof-reading.

I am very grateful to Miss Eileen Howard, Mrs. Marian Perry and Mrs. Harriet Kelley for their devoted interest throughout the project and their generous help in typing the manuscript.

My husband was very happy with the co-operation he was given in the Department of Psychology at Tufts University—not just in constructing apparatus and designing experiments and using statistics but in the general sympathetic understanding given to his work. His long-time association with Dr. John A. Hanson was of the greatest value in carrying out his research in kinaesthesia. And more recently, Dr. Richard A. Brown has given significant assistance in both teaching and research. He has given much time and thought to the preparation of the bibliography, the glossary and the index.

I cannot adequately thank all the people who have helped in the writing of this book, but I would like to record my profound appreciation and thanks to the following people: Dr. Mason N. Crook, Dr. John L. Kennedy, Dr. Leonard C. Mead, Dr. Dorothea Crook, Dr. Philip B. Sampson, Miss Florence E. Gray, Professor James O'Leary, Mr. Donald N. O'Connell, Professor Sam McLaughlin, Dr. Paul G. Ronco, Dr. Arthur Uhlir, Jr., Mr. Max Hirshkowitz, Professor Morris

S. Schwartz, Mr. Lester Thompson, Mr. Peter Elbow, Miss Marjorie
L. Barstow, Mr. Richard M. Gummere, Jr., Mr. Edward Maisel, Mr.
Goddard Binkley, Mr. Joe Armstrong, Mr. Beaumont Alexander, Mr.
M. R. M. Alexander, Miss Irene Tasker, Miss Margaret Goldie; Mr. W.
H. M. Carrington, Mr. Alexander D. Murray, Mr. Patrick J.
Macdonald, Miss Irene Stewart, Mrs. Erika Whittaker, and Mr. Felix
Morrow.

HELEN RUMSEY JONES
1976

1

Escape from the Monkey Trap: An Introduction to the Alexander Technique

In an expanding system, such as a growing organism . . . freedom to change the pattern of performance is one of the intrinsic properties of the organization itself.

C. Judson Herrick

I see
The lost are like this, and their scourge to be
As I am mine, their sweating selves; but worse.

Gerard Manley Hopkins

What can I do to be saved? This is an old question and there has never been a shortage of answers. The question is still being asked and the answers continue to multiply: meditate; join a group; relax ("You must relax"); scream; have an orgasm; take your clothes off; lie on a bed and kick; have a massage; give someone else a massage; confess your sins; do isometric exercises; do isotonic exercises; be your own best friend; take a pill. Which shall I choose? Is one way, or combination of ways, better than any other? Or is the important thing to be doing something, regardless of what? What is the fashionable way this year? Is structural integration still in? Or should I try bioenergetics instead? What if I try them both and find that I haven't really changed at all; that I am still "my sweating self but worse"?

With so much competition it seems providential that the Alexander Technique, which had its fashionable hour as a New Way of Life back in the 1920s, is still available and has not been choked out or absorbed by other and newer ways. For the Alexander Technique doesn't teach you something new to do. It teaches you how to bring more practical intelligence into what you are already doing; how to eliminate stereotyped responses; how to deal with habit and change. It leaves you free to choose your own goal but gives you a better use of yourself while you work toward it.

F. Matthias Alexander (1869-1955) discovered a method (a "means-whereby") for expanding consciousness to take in inhibition as well as excitation ("not-doing" as well as "doing") and thus obtain a better integration of the reflex and voluntary elements in a response pattern. The procedure makes any movement or activity smoother and easier, and is strongly reinforcing. Alexander and his brother, A. R. Alexander (1874–1947), developed a way of using their hands to convey information directly through the kinaesthetic sense. They gave their pupils an immediate "aha" experience of performing a habitual act—walking, talking, breathing, handling objects, and the like—in a non-habitual way. The technique changed the underlying feeling tone of a movement, producing a kinaesthetic effect of lightness that was pleasurable and rewarding and served as the distinguishing hallmark of non-habitual responses. It was then up to the pupil to learn the technique for himself. The learning process was greatly facilitated, however, because in the first lesson the pupil had a foretaste of the experiences he would have, once he had learned it.

F. M. Alexander published four books between 1910 and 1941. In them he presented a unified view of the organism, strongly opposed to any form of mind-body dualism. He maintained that under the influence of civilization, man as a whole—as a human being—had degenerated, that he had reached a stage where his instincts were no longer reliable, and that if he was going to survive, his behaviour had to be reintegrated on a conscious level. He labelled contemporary therapeutic and educational methods as "end-gaining," because they were based on analytical concepts that divided the organism and produced results whose undesirable side effects outweighed their benefits. He proposed instead a "means-whereby" principle in which inhibition of stereotyped responses opens the way for conscious direction and control. The principle need not be inconsistent with specific therapies, but the means-whereby (inhibition) has to come first. No matter how many specific ends you may gain, you are worse off than before, he maintained, if in the process of gaining them you have destroyed the integrity of the organism.

Though it was John Dewey who introduced Alexander's books to the American public, his ideas have had little influence on educational theory or practice. They have made a greater impact on the newer body-mind therapies where his precepts about non-end-gaining and the danger of neglecting the body in favour of the mind hold a prominent place. In none of them, however, does there appear to be any grasp of his basic discovery. It is quite possible to accept on a verbal level the idea of mind-body unity and the principle of non-end-gaining without increasing your own self-knowledge and control (or what Alexander meant by self-knowledge and control). The non-verbal aspect of the Technique has always been a stumbling block to readers who felt that Alexander was holding something back from them and that there was more there than the books conveyed. Dewey and Huxley and other early advocates were frustrated in their attempts to describe the Technique because they could not convey the sensory experiences it involved.

Alexander was fully aware of the unique character of his teaching. He had, in fact, attempted to take out patents on it, and for many years it was not possible to study the Technique (apart from reading the books) except with him and his brother. In the 1930s, however, he decided to start a three-year training course for teachers in which they could learn to communicate the new use of themselves which he and his brother had developed. He continued the training of teachers until his death in 1955. Since then, training courses have been set up by some of his pupils and there are now a hundred or more teachers with certificates signed by F. M. or A. R. Alexander or by someone whom they trained.

Most of the literature on the subject, including Alexander's own books, while stressing the preventive character of the Technique, have used as illustrations the same kind of case histories and postural before-and-after photographs that are used to prove the value of other methods. Such records, of course, are worth obtaining and reporting, since they show that *post hoc* changes actually take place. They do not throw any light, however, on the mechanisms by which the changes come about or on the nature of the kinaesthetic experiences that pupils report. To remedy this situation a study was made at the Tufts Institute for Experimental Psychology. Rejecting as criteria the long-term changes that are claimed for other forms of training, we chose instead to study the changes in movement pattern and performance and the reported changes in feeling tone that can be produced immediately (that is, without previous training). Using quantitative measures and control groups, we were able to construct an operational definition of the technique and suggest a mechanism to account for the changes. We believe that the study supports John Dewey's opinion of the scientific importance of Alexander's discovery and should lead to further scientific investigation of the technique.

In this book I want to describe the essential features of the Alexander Technique—those that distinguish it from other approaches to the mind-body problem. The knowledge should be available to teachers and therapists because of its unique power for dealing with habit and change—for dealing with the person who "sees the better course and approves of it but continues to follow the worse," who wants to change but is convinced he cannot.

It is said that a simple way to trap a monkey is to present him with a nut in a bottle. The monkey puts his paw through the bottle's narrow mouth, grasps the nut, then cannot withdraw his paw because he will not (and hence cannot) let go of the nut. Most people are caught in monkey traps of unconscious habit. They cannot escape because they do not perceive what they are doing while they are doing it. Having an unconscious response pattern pointed out to you by somebody else is not the same thing as perceiving it for yourself while it is happening. The Alexander Technique opens a window onto the little-known area between stimulus and response and gives you the self-knowledge you need in order to change the pattern of your response—or, if you choose, not to make it at all.

2

Sensory Evidence

*At times also I have been put to confusion and driven to despair
of ever explaining something for which I could not account but
which my senses told me to be true.*

Galileo, *Two New Sciences*

AN EXPERIENCED TEACHER can demonstrate the kinaesthetic effect
of lightness, which is the hallmark of the Alexander Technique, in a
relatively short time, often within a few minutes. For such a demonstration, it is best to use a naïve subject, since the effect is heightened
if it is unexpected.

Applying a light pressure with his hands, the demonstrator
changes the balance (or poise) of the subject's head in such a way
that the muscles in the nape of the neck lengthen, allowing the head
to rotate slightly forward as it moves up from the shoulders. Care
must be taken not to set up stretch reflexes in the muscles by using
too much pressure or applying pressure too rapidly. Properly carried
out, the procedure will establish a new dynamic balance between the
weight of the head and the tonus of the muscles so that within a
limited range (greater in some subjects than in others) the head
behaves like an inertial system which can move or be moved freely
in any direction without a feeling of weight.

The demonstrator then helps the subject to continue the
changed relation between the head and trunk during a few everyday movements like walking, sitting down and standing up, or raising his arms. In the process the subject's body can be felt by the
demonstrator to lengthen and become lighter. Subjects regularly
report that the movements are easier and smoother and that they
feel lighter and taller while they are doing them. "More ease and
lightness," "a feeling of ease, of competence—very different from

'relaxation'," "a greater degree of ease and consequent pleasure," are expressions that subjects have used to describe the experience. The feeling of pleasure in an everyday movement takes most subjects by surprise, and their faces break spontaneously into a smile as they notice it. "It's a funny thing," one of them said. "It's as if my arms liked moving this way and wanted to do it again." To some subjects the idea of moving against gravity (as in getting up from a chair) without effort is difficult to grasp—"a source of wonderment." In describing the experience, one said: "First I was sitting down, and then I was standing up. I don't know how I got there." "The movement seemed absolutely impossible," another reported, "until you had performed it, when it was unbelievably simple—like walking straight into a wall only to find when you reached it that there was no wall and you had passed through into the space beyond."

The kinaesthetic effect can be demonstrated for almost any activity performed within the gravitational field. Some teachers, however, prefer to eliminate gravity as much as possible and to work with the subject lying on a table, manipulating various parts of his body while he inhibits his habitual response to the stimulus to move. So far as I know, the Alexander brothers never did "lying-down-work" of this kind unless they had a pupil who was bedridden. In my observation, it gives a wrong first impression of the Technique, as if it were a form of relaxation therapy.

Huxley and others have begged off altogether from describing the kinaesthetic effect on the ground that you can't impart a sensory experience to someone who has not had it himself. It would be, said Huxley, like describing the colour red to someone who was colour blind. While it is true that another person's kinaesthetic experience— the way a movement feels to him—cannot be shared, the movement itself can be studied objectively. The colour red, to use Huxley's example, can be described objectively as light of a given range of wavelengths. In a similar fashion, the objective physical conditions corresponding to different kinaesthetic experiences can be obtained by multiple-image photography of movement patterns. In the series of experiments described in Chapter 12, I succeeded in quantifying the physical dimensions (patterns of movement in time and space) that correspond to the kinaesthetic experiences of lightness, smoothness and ease reported during the guided movements.

The sensory effect of lightness which accompanies the guided movements persists often for hours and sometimes for days, affecting the patterns of all subsequent movements. If it is not renewed, however, the effect ultimately fades out and the subject reverts to his habitual movement patterns. The significance of the experience can be grasped only if it is followed up and used as a device for self-examination and for initiating a programme of change. The easiest way for me to indicate the nature of the change is to narrate some of my own experiences in studying the Technique.

My first experience of making a habitual movement without habitual effort seems as vivid to me now as it was when A. R. Alexander demonstrated the Technique to me in 1938. Perhaps it was the element of surprise that made the experience so memorable. I had expected something quite different—to have my faults of breathing and voice production diagnosed and to be given a set of exercises to correct them. Instead, Alexander chose the movement from sitting to standing for his demonstration. He made a few slight changes in the way I was sitting (they seemed quite arbitrary to me and I could not remember afterward what they were), then, asking me to leave my head as it was, he initiated the upward movement without further instruction. Before I had a chance to organize my habitual response, the movement was completed and I found myself standing in a position that felt strangely comfortable. I was fully conscious throughout the movement, and it was a consciousness, not of being moved by someone else—Alexander appeared to be making no effort whatever—but by a set of reflexes whose operation I knew nothing about.

In addition to the reflex effect, the movement was notable for the way time and space were perceived. Though it took less time than usual to complete the movement, the rate at which I moved seemed paradoxically slower and more controlled and the trajectories that my head and trunk followed were unfamiliar. The impression was that of a sudden expansion in both dimensions, so that more time and space were available for the movement.

The most striking aspect of the movement, however, was the sensory effect of lightness that it induced. The feeling had not been present at the start, nor had it been suggested to me; it was clearly a direct effect of the movement. While it lasted, everything I did, including breathing, became easier. After a short time the effect faded away, leaving me, however, with the certainty that I had glimpsed a new world of experience which had more to offer than the limited set of movement patterns, attitudes and responses to which I was accustomed.

This is not a case history and I am not going to describe in detail the symptoms, mental and physical, that bothered me. None of them responded to therapy and I had been advised that the best thing I could do was learn to live with them. Though reluctant to accept this advice, I had begun to think of myself at thirty-three as a semi-invalid. My principle problem was fatigue. Though I thoroughly enjoyed my work, which was teaching and research, the physical activities of daily life—walking, talking, sitting at a desk—fatigued me unduly. I had not stopped looking for a cure (that was why I had consulted A. R. in the first place), but I had no real hope of finding one. The only remedy that had proved effective in the past was rest, but it was not a real solution. As soon as I resumed activity and began responding to familiar stimuli, the symptoms returned. It had occurred to me that my manner of responding to stimuli might be responsible for my difficulties, but attempts to change the way I did things always ended up by my doing them "a different kind of badly," as John Dewey put it.

My chronic state of fatigue undoubtedly heightened by contrast the sensory effect of lightness that A. R. demonstrated. In positive terms the effect could be described as a sense of well-being and of pleasure in movement. At the time, however, I could perceive it only as the absence of sensations that had accompanied the movement in the past. I was not aware of any voluntary action except a negative one. Alexander had asked me not to alter the position of my head and I had not done so. The significance of this fact became apparent when I tried to repeat the movement.

As soon as the goal of standing up was in my mind, I got set for it by bringing my head closer to my shoulders and started pushing off with the same amount of effort I had used in the past. This preliminary set seemed so inevitable and natural that I would not have noticed it at all if I had not just had the experience of moving without it. Once it had been brought to my attention, however, I discovered what seemed almost a compulsion to shorten the muscles at the back of my neck and displace my head downward as a preliminary to any movement that required effort (or that I thought required effort). In spite of the demonstration I had just had, there seemed to be only two alternatives: to shorten muscles and get set for the movement or not to move at all. After I was aware of the problem, A. R. varied his approach, asking me not to get up but to allow him to move me while I inhibited any increase in neck-muscle tension. At first this seemed equally difficult. The instant I felt myself moving I forgot my resolution and began thinking about getting up. In doing so I fell into my old pattern of tension and got ready for the effort I had always made. When I tried to prevent this response by relaxing, I found that I had again displaced my head and had succeeded only in making myself a dead weight.

I will not describe here the devices that A. R. employed to bring me out of this impasse and get me to "think in activity." The big stumbling block for me lay in my concept of thinking. Thinking meant concentrating, narrowing the attention to a small area and making an effort to keep it there.

Francis Bacon said that in a scientific investigation "it would be an unsound fancy and self-contradictory to think that things which have never yet been done can be done except by means which have never yet been tried. " I was trying to do something I had never done before—to get up consciously without effort. But the means I was using, concentration, was not new. It was what I had always used in attempting to solve my problems. Obviously it was not working now. When I concentrated either on myself or on the goal I wanted to reach, something happened outside my field of attention to frustrate my attempt. It was only after I realized attention can be expanded as well as narrowed that I began to note progress. In order to move on a conscious level in which I could be aware of both doing and not-doing (of the inhibitory as well as the excitatory part of the movement), I had to expand my attention so that it took in something of myself and something of the environment as well. It was just as easy, I found, instead of setting up two fields—one for the self (introspection) and another for the environment (extraspection)—to establish a single integrated field in which both the environment and the self could be viewed simultaneously. At the start I could not extend the field very far or maintain it very long, but whenever I succeeded in establishing it I was able to follow A. R.'s instruction and inhibit my immediate response to the stimulus to stand up and could maintain the inhibition long enough either to let him initiate and guide the movement for me or (with somewhat more difficulty) to initiate it and carry it out myself. In either case the movement induced the same kinaesthetic effect of lightness—not as sharp as the first time because the element of surprise was missing, but more enduring.

Once I had experienced the kinaesthetic effect, the reward was so great that I tried to recapture it directly and to hang on to it when I had it. This proved self-defeating, however. It was the indirect effect of a psycho-physical process and could only be obtained by not trying for it. Its chief function in the learning process was to indicate by its presence that I was on the right track and to provide a background of feeling tone against which maladaptive response patterns could be recognized for what they were. I had been aware of neck-muscle tension before but had not been aware that the tension increased in response to stimuli. Now the response pattern—the increment in tension—began to stand out against the newly induced background of postural tone so that there was a clear-cut figure-ground relation between them. What the procedures I learned from A. R. had done was to remove a great deal of the "noise" from the tonic "ground" so that the tensional "figure" was easier to perceive. Once the figure was perceived for what it was—an increment of tension in response to a particular stimulus—it could be controlled; "inhibited" was the word A. R. used.

After I had clearly perceived the pattern of neck-muscle tension and understood the part it played in one everyday movement, I began to notice it in other movements. It appeared when I started to sit down as well as when I started to stand up. I noticed it sharply in climbing stairs, in picking up a suitcase, in taking a deep breath, in writing a letter. Less sharply but unmistakably, the pattern appeared in everything I did. When it was inhibited, the same effect followed as in the first movement that had been demonstrated to me. The pattern was not confined to the neck. The neck was merely the distribution point at which the increase in tension began and from which it spread like a net to other parts of the body. I noticed it particularly in my arms and shoulders, the small of my back, and the adductor muscles in my legs. The significance of the neck was that the pattern began there, in time as well as in space, and if it did not begin there, it could not be propagated to the rest of the body.

Inhibition is a negative term, but it describes a positive process. By refusing to respond to a stimulus in a habitual way you release a set of reflexes that lengthen the body and facilitate movement. The immediate result of Alexandrian inhibition is a sense of freedom, as if a heavy garment that had been hampering all of your movements has been removed. The image that occurred to me after Alexander's demonstration was that of Cardinal Ballou in Louis XI's cage, a cage constructed so as to keep him from achieving his full length in any direction. It suddenly seemed to me that I had spent my life in such a cage and had just found the key to get out.

In describing their experiences pupils are apt to emphasize physical changes—so much so that the Technique is often thought of as a kind of posture training. I think this is natural, especially for intellectuals who tend to be overawed by the physical changes that lessons produce. In my case, the discovery that physical activity could be a source of pleasure was like waking from a bad dream. In the past I had taken exercise of one kind or another, because doctors had recommended it, but I did not enjoy it. Now the situation had changed. Using my body even for such tasks as shovelling snow or mowing the lawn became pleasurable. I supposed that other people had these experiences routinely, but for me they carried the fresh appeal of newness—like a new spectrum of colours. There was more to it, however, than mere sensory experience; there was a strong intellectual content. By expanding the field of consciousness it is possible to enjoy an experience at both a sensory and an intellectual level. By "overviewing" it you can detect and inhibit trains of thought or patterns of tension that otherwise would get in the way of your enjoyment. Bringing the intellect into physical experience has practical value as a problem-solving technique. A sprained ankle or a stiff neck ceases to be mysterious. After ruling out external causes that can be remedied by help from outside, you set up the hypothesis that something you are doing is interfering with the healing process. It is a hypothesis that can be easily tested and acted upon.

Having injured my back in an car accident, I had never been able to sit at a desk for any length of time without discomfort. Now I began to notice that whenever I leaned forward to read or write I displaced my head downward and allowed my chest to collapse so that my torso was a dead weight on my lower back. Since I had always done this, I assumed that there was no alternative except to make an effort to sit up straight. After experimenting with the Technique I discovered that if I inhibited the preliminary displacement of my head I could move forward without becoming heavy and could work at my desk without discomfort. I got similar results when I applied these procedures to the respiratory problems that I had had since childhood. Though A. R. did not mention breathing, I noticed almost from the first lesson that I was breathing more easily than I was accustomed to. At one point I realized that my head was not in the plane it was usually in, that air was coming through my nose instead of my mouth, and that muscles attached to my rib-cage were being stretched. I instinctively tried to pull my head back to its accustomed position but A. R. prevented me. This gave me the panicky feeling that I could not breathe at all, though I knew that my lungs were filling and emptying. The panic persisted until I gradually accepted the fact that breathing could take place without the neck-muscle tension to which I was so long accustomed. I could not get this effect, however, if I tried to relax these muscles directly. It was only by making a total change in the relation between head and trunk and shifting the centre of attention away from breathing that the change would take place. The effect on breathing was a powerful incentive to maintain the new use of myself that A. R. initiated and to keep me from slipping back into my old attitudes. Several years later on a sultry day in August I tried experimentally with the help of a mirror to reconstruct my old way of standing. I soon gave it up when I realized that I had brought on an asthmatic attack, the first since I began lessons. I did not repeat the experiment.

The physical effects of the Technique are the easiest to describe and measure, but the psychological effects are of greater importance. Some of them can be explained merely as side effects—changes in mental attitude which follow an improvement in health. You are less depressed when you are not physically weighed down. Your image of yourself improves when you feel physically more competent. You find that you like other people more when you become more relaxed about yourself. Such changes, which are regularly reported by pupils, are not unlike changes that are reported for other therapies. In addition to automatic changes of this nature I experienced an almost immediate increase in mental and emotional control.

Mind wandering was a problem that in my case was beginning to get out of hand. When I was following a line of reasoning, listening to a lecture, or trying to reach a decision, I was continually being diverted by some association of ideas and floating off on a stream of thought without direction or control, often ending up in an emotional reaction that was unwanted and unproductive. I had long recognized the problem, but I did not know how to attack it. None of the therapies that were fashionable at the time sounded hopeful to me—all of them focused on the past. Even before I met Alexander I had decided that it did not matter whether Pavlov was right or Freud was right—the problem of change had to be solved in the ongoing present.

Early lessons in the Alexander Technique gave me a new insight into the problem when I found that the paradigm of inhibition that had been demonstrated for physical movement could be applied equally well when the activity would be classed as mental or emotional. The field of attention has a set of kinaesthetic coordinates which supply a framework for thinking. If my thoughts were pulled off the track (as they so frequently were) into irrelevancy, the change in direction of thinking registered kinaesthetically as a disturbance in the level of tonus and my thought could be brought back before it had progressed very far along its stream of associations.

Because the field of attention is not simply a theoretical construct but a kinaesthetically perceptible state of tonus, any emotional disturbance affects it immediately and can often be perceived as a change in the level of muscle tone before a reaction in the autonomic system has begun. Anger, for example, has a characteristic pattern that is easily recognizable. In one lesson I was suddenly aware that I was twitching with anger at something A. R. was saying (he was trying, no doubt, to provoke a reaction) and that the muscles in my neck and shoulders were being strongly activated. It was the same pattern that I had noticed before when A. R. was trying to get me to stand up in a coordinated way. This time instead of trying to control my anger (which I thought was well justified) I turned my attention to my neck and shoulders. I found that I could inhibit a further increase of tension and allow the muscles to lengthen; and that as long as I did this I could carry on a rational conversation in spite of my inward agitation. It was an altogether different process from suppressing anger, which used to tie me into a knot. The emotion (or the autonomic manifestation of it), instead of building up to an explosive force, remained a potential for action but did not interfere with rational decision. The same procedure could be used to take the panic out of fear. Redirecting or containing an emotion in this way is not the same thing as relaxing or ignoring the stimulus, both of which would reduce the capacity for action if action should be needed.

F. M. Alexander called this process "keeping in touch with your reason." A great deal of ingenuity has gone into developing biofeedback devices for controlling various parts of the autonomic system directly. Alexandrian inhibition works indirectly. Skeletal muscles (neck muscles in particular) serve as both monitor and effector, leaving the behaviour of the autonomic system to the "wisdom of the body."

The changes that I observed in myself were often unexpected, but they were never accompanied by any sudden or violent release of emotion and never left me feeling defenceless. The Alexander Technique provides the knowledge and freedom to change, but it is change within a developmental model. There is no "must." Changes take place when you are ready for them and can permit them to happen. Habitual tensions that have grown up over a long period of time limit development and prevent the free expression of personality. They serve as a protection, however, in situations where, rightly or wrongly, a person feels vulnerable or incompetent. The Alexander Technique does not deprive one of this "character armouring" as long as it is needed. Lessons in the Technique release an organic process of change that gradually replaces old rigid habits with new habits which are flexible and can themselves be changed. The process of change is not mindless. It can be directed by intelligence into paths that lead to the best development of the individual's own personality.

When I was convinced from repeated experience that the Technique really worked—that my intelligence could be used to solve my problems on all levels—my outlook on life changed. My satisfaction in the discovery was incomplete, however, because I could not formulate what I knew so as to communicate it to others. Montaigne, who found the pleasure of self-examination to be the greatest of all pleasures, invented the essay in order to convey his pleasure to others. I knew from experience, however, that words were not adequate to convey the meaning of the Alexander Technique. Besides a better understanding of the mechanism by which change was effected, I had to learn how to use my hands. The opportunity to do so was offered to me when F. M. Alexander came to the United States in the fall of 1940.

3

Alexander's Discovery

*This story of perceptiveness, of intelligence, and of persistence,
shown by a man without medical training, is one of the true epics
of medical research and practice.*

N. Tinbergen

IN THE EARLY 1890s Frederick Matthias (F. M.) Alexander was
giving one-man shows in Sydney and Melbourne, Australia. Readings
from Shakespeare were his specialty, and he was particularly fond of
Hamlet and *The Merchant of Venice.* Early in his career he began to have
trouble with his throat and vocal cords. Friends told him that they
could hear him gasp and suck in air through his mouth when he
recited, and on one occasion he became so hoarse by the end of the
evening that he could scarcely speak.

Rest and medication, which his doctor prescribed, were effective only until he went back to the platform, when the hoarseness
promptly returned. He reasoned from this that it must be something
he did while reciting that caused the trouble, and since no one
seemed able to tell him what it was, he decided to find out for himself. Standing in front of a mirror he watched himself both in ordinary speaking and in reciting. At first he noticed nothing in ordinary
speaking, but when he launched into one of his recitations, he saw
that several things were happening that he had not seen before: He
was depressing his larynx and audibly sucking in breath; he was lifting his chest and hollowing his back; and he was changing the axis
of his head by lifting his chin and rotating the head "backward and
down." Once he had discovered these tendencies, he found that they
were present, though to a lesser degree, in ordinary speaking. Having
tried unsuccessfully to deal with each of them separately, he finally
came to the conclusion that they were interrelated parts of a total

pattern of which the principal part was the change in the axis of the head. When he could keep from pulling back his head in ordinary speaking, the tendency to suck in breath and depress the larynx decreased and the condition of his larynx and vocal cords improved. Convinced by this experience that he was on the right track, he determined to pursue the investigation further until he could establish a reliable control over his speaking voice. Adding two more mirrors to the system so that he could observe himself in profile, he realized that his response to the stimulus to speak was indeed a total pattern, for it involved an increase in muscle tension everywhere. To deal with the problem, he devised a set of "directions" (messages from the brain to the various mechanisms) for relaxing muscles in his neck instead of tensing them, allowing his head to go "forward and up" instead of pulling it backward and down, lengthening his spine instead of arching it, and widening his back instead of narrowing it. These directions (or "orders" as he often called them) were to be projected both sequentially and simultaneously ("one after another and all at once"); that is, he would continue giving the directions for the first part while giving the directions for the second part and so on. He practised giving himself these directions for long periods of time, "even months," he tells us, without trying to "do" them. Finally, believing that he had mastered the problem, he applied the new "means-whereby" to reciting but was disappointed to discover from the mirrors that as soon as he began to recite he reverted to his old response pattern and pulled his head back and down. From this and from similar experiences with the mirrors he concluded that his senses were unreliable and that he could not depend on instinctive or habitual guidance if he wanted to make a change. His final step was to bring the whole process of inhibiting and directing onto the conscious level and keep it there, deciding at the last instant whether or not to gain his original end and speak, or to change the end and do something different such as lifting his hand. Whichever choice he made, he would continue to project the directions. These procedures, he said, would result in a different activity from the old, habitual activity "in that the old activity could not be controlled outside the gaining of a given end, whereas the new activity could be controlled for the gaining of any end that was consciously desired."

This is a compressed account of how F. M. Alexander discovered his technique of conscious control. The account is a paradigm for bringing the pattern of a learned response (any learned response) onto the conscious level where it can be controlled in such a way that when the associated stimulus is presented, three choices are available: to make the response as it was originally learned; to make a different and more appropriate response; not to respond at all. The procedure, Alexander said, is contrary to all learning procedures that have been followed in the past.

He concluded his account by saying: "After I had worked on this plan for a considerable time, I became free from my tendency to revert to my wrong habitual use in reciting, and the marked effect of this upon my functioning convinced me that I was at last on the right track, for once free from this tendency, I also became free from the throat and vocal trouble and from the respiratory and nasal difficulties with which I had been beset from birth."

Secure in the control of his voice, Alexander resumed his career of reciting but continued to experiment with the new technique for monitoring his performance, extending it beyond speaking into other psycho-physical activities. In the course of time he began to share his observations with other actors and reciters (public recitation was a popular profession at that time) and soon was teaching his method on a professional basis.

About this time he was joined by his brother, A. R. (Albert Redden) Alexander. A. R., who was five years younger than F. M., had run away from school to take part in the gold rush to western Australia. After many adventures (in one of which he lost a finger on his left hand) he came down with typhoid, which left him with weakened eyesight, and he returned without taking up the claim he had staked. F. M., who wanted a partner to help him develop and exploit his discovery, taught A. R. what he had learned. (A. R. maintained that he needed only six lessons.) The two brothers experimented with each other and together worked out various procedures and instructions, which were incorporated into the Technique. A. R. told me that the words his brother used in his books to describe the teaching procedures were very carefully chosen and tested out, and he, A. R., didn't think they could be improved on. The two brothers worked together for about six years, teaching alternately in Melbourne and

Sydney. The partnership was interrupted at one time when A. R. went off to South Africa to fight in the Boer War. When he returned, F. M. was thinking of moving to London. His teaching practice had continued to expand and its emphasis to shift from voice control to the control of reaction generally. Several doctors had begun referring patients to him because of the application to therapy that they saw in the Technique. One of them, Dr. J. W. Stewart McKay, a prominent surgeon in Sydney, persuaded F. M. to go to London in order to bring his technique before a larger public. He left Australia, never to return, and arrived in London in the spring of 1904, with letters of introduction to actors and physicians. A. R. followed him and the two again set up a joint practice, with teaching rooms at Army & Navy Mansions on Victoria Street. (They moved a few years later to 16 Ashley Place, S. W. 1, where F. M. continued to teach until he died.) F. M. had little difficulty establishing his teaching methods among members of the theatrical profession; and most of the leading actors of the day came to him for lessons at various times. Sir Henry Irving used to keep him in the wings while he was on stage in order to have his professional help between acts. Alexander told me that he used to sit with a book in his hands, threatening to throw it at Irving if he pulled his head back while he was speaking. "He knew that I would do it, too," he added.

Not willing to limit himself to coaching actors, F. M. soon began actively promoting his ideas and his practice with letters to the press (he recommended this to me as an easy way to bring new ideas before the public) and by articles he had privately printed. In 1906 and 1907 he published two pamphlets on "respiratory re-education" and another in 1908, "Re-education of the Kinaesthetic Systems." Most of the basic features of his teaching and much of the language are to be found in these three pamphlets. The problem he took up first was how to restore normal respiration, but realizing that "nature does not work in parts but treats everything as a whole," he decided that it was necessary to re-educate the whole person in order to accomplish a fundamental change. His thesis was that every normal child possessed at birth the conditions necessary for healthy development. (A newborn child who was a "bad breather," he said elsewhere, was not normal, but the bad breathing could not be treated or diagnosed apart from the imperfect coordination generally.) If, however, the child's natural activity was not encouraged and intelligently directed, his kinaesthesia would soon become "demoralized" by the bad habits of the school room and the "crouching positions necessitated by useless and irrational desk work." The result of the demoralizing conditions of schools and offices and of modern civilized life in general has been a faulty pattern of breathing associated with postural imbalance—"undue rigidity" in certain muscle groups and "undue flaccidity" in others. This unfortunate condition, Alexander polemically maintained, has been made very much worse by "deep breathing and physical culture exercises," which have added to the postural imbalance by increasing the muscular rigidity. (Relaxation exercises, on the other hand, merely increase the imbalance in the other direction.) He was particularly severe in the condemnation of the deep-breathing exercises then much in vogue. Such exercises, he said, encourage sniffing air through the nose and gasping it through the mouth, habits that lead to, among other things, a collapse of the nostrils (the alae nasi), a depression of the larynx, and a throwing back of the head to open the mouth. (How common these conditions still are can be seen by watching almost any group of singers or wind players on the television screen.) The whole concept behind the deep-breathing exercises was wrong. They were aimed at producing a great expansion of the chest without any consideration for adequate contraction, which is equally important. Besides bad respiratory conditions like emphysema, faulty breathing habits, Alexander said, have produced a variety of postural deformities ("pot-belly attitudes," Bernard Shaw called them) and a general deterioration of the muscular and nervous systems because of imperfect oxygenation of the blood.

Since breathing was an ongoing activity of the organism as a whole and a function of general coordination, it could not be improved by picking out one phase of the cycle, the downward excursion of the diaphragm, for example, and devising exercises to strengthen it. That would only unbalance the breathing process in a different way and create new problems of mal-coordination. The reason, Alexander said, that re-education procedures usually failed was that they did not take into consideration the wrong mental attitudes that were inextricably bound up with wrong physical conditions. If a person was mal-coordinated, he would not have a reliable sensory standard to guide him in making a change. In trying to carry out the instructions for a specific exercise he would use far too much effort and this would produce side effects as undesirable as the original conditions the exercise was supposed to correct. In the pamphlets Alexander explained that it was to deal with this important problem of "faulty sensory appreciation" that he had developed his technique. Unlike other methods of re-education, his was designed to correct both the mental attitude and the physical condition at the same time by combining "directive orders" on the part of the pupil (to change the mental attitude) with skilful manipulation on the part of the teacher (to change the physical condition). The directive orders activated the ideomotor centres in the brain without initiating movement. They were of two kinds: 1) negative (inhibitory), which served to prevent the old habit ("what is not to be done"), and 2) the positive command, which would ensure the posture specifically correct for the pupil. The two sets of orders were essentially one, with the negative order (inhibition) primary and the positive order subordinate to it.

The pupil was instructed to give his attention exclusively to the orders (the means-whereby) and not to concentrate on the end or goal to be reached. The teacher would then bring the pupil into a "position of mechanical advantage" in which the back was widened and the spine more extended. In such a position breathing would be facilitated and stiffening of the neck and arms and other postural faults would be reduced. Alexander claimed that with a pupil who employed his powers of inhibition adequately and rehearsed the orders correctly a skilful teacher could bring about truly remarkable changes. Such a system of re-education, he maintained, not only would correct bad breathing habits but could be used to overcome the effects of "faulty child and adolescent modes of existence"—that is, habits that interfere with mature behaviour.

One of the procedures the Alexanders developed at this time is what they called "the whispered ah." As they used it in their teaching, it is an extremely effective device for demonstrating the rôle of inhibition in breathing and voice production. After a pupil has gained sufficient conscious control so that he can follow a set of instructions without shortening neck muscles and changing the axis of his head, he is asked 1) to notice where his tongue is and to leave it with the tip touching his lower teeth; 2) to smile by thinking of something funny (a stage smile will not do) in order to relax his lips and free the passages leading to the throat; 3) to open his mouth by letting the lower jaw move forward and down (gravity should do most of the work) and not by tilting the head back; 4) to produce the sound of "ah" in a whisper (a sound chosen because it was not associated with ordinary bad habits of vocalization); 5) to close the lips and let air come in through the nose. The Alexanders maintained that they did not use exercises, but they made an exception in the case of the "whispered ah" because it is primarily an exercise in inhibition and "non-end-gaining". The pupil's attention, which has been expanded to take in the head–neck–trunk relation, is focused on each sequential event in turn and is not allowed to jump ahead to the end to be gained, the whispered sound, which is merely one event in the series, without any more or less importance than the others. With his attention organized in this way the pupil can detect and inhibit any unnecessary tension or effort like lifting his chest or depressing it, or tilting back his head and sucking in air, which has grown around the acts of breathing and voice production and become unconscious and habitual. Taking a breath, it should be noted, comes not at the beginning but at the end of the sequence and then is allowed to take place reflexly. The procedure is not difficult to master. It can be varied by substituting other sounds, either whispered or voiced. And it can be used as a model for studying and improving the performance of other activities in which reflex and voluntary elements are imperfectly integrated.

4

Man's Supreme Inheritance

*The great phase in man's advancement is that in which he passes
from subconscious to conscious control of his own mind and body.*
F. M. Alexander, *Man's Supreme Inheritance*

THERE WERE DOCTORS in London who were aware that orthodox
methods of breathing control were unsatisfactory and who were quite
willing to send patients to the Alexanders. If F. M. had been more
conciliatory in his pronouncements about medical treatment, he
might have won a place for his system of respiratory re-education
within the medical perimeter. He was far from humble, however, and
had no intention of taking a subservient position like a physiothera-
pist. He had no doubts about the value of what he had to offer, and
if doctors refused to investigate his claims, they and their patients,
he believed, were the losers. This arrogance from "an Australian
actor" won him more enemies than friends among doctors, but from
the start there were always a few who became his pupils, sent him
patients, and wrote tributes to his work for the medical press.
Alexander published another pamphlet on breathing in 1909, but
after that he stopped appealing to the medical profession directly
and turned to the educated public. In *Man's Supreme Inheritance*
(1910) he made a quantum leap from therapy to philosophy.
    Much has been made of Alexander's lack of academic training.
"More or less self-educated," he described himself in *Who's Who*. He
was far from ignorant, however. Though he had rejected the opportunity to study physiology and anatomy because he could tell from
their appearance that the knowledge had not done the men who
taught it any good, he managed to acquire a respectable amount of
information (perhaps from some of his pupils) about the structure
and functioning, normal and pathological, of the human body. "The

physiological side of my technique," he wrote, "has been the subject of friendly discussion between medical men and physiologists, and I am not aware of any physiological findings having been advanced which are at variance with any of its procedures" (*The Universal Constant in Living*, p. 136). His explanation of respiratory mechanisms, though written in layman's language, is simple and lucid, and its accuracy has not been challenged by anatomists. His idea of how a living organism ought to function must owe a good deal to his knowledge of animals, wild and domestic. He and his brother were brought up with horses, and both of them were familiar with the wild game of the Australian bush. His literary taste was formed on Byron, Shakespeare and the Bible. Contemporary authors whom he read with the most interest and approval were Herbert Spencer, T. H. Huxley and Sir James Frazer. He may also have been familiar with William James, and he had great hope for the "young science of psychology."

Alexander's readings in anthropology and evolutionary thought combined with his observations of contemporary man brought him to the thesis that he advanced in *Man's Supreme Inheritance*. Simply stated, the thesis is that "the great phase in man's advancement is that in which he passes from subconscious to conscious control of his own mind and body." Animals evolved through mechanisms of subconscious control in accordance with the laws of selective evolution. The same laws continued to operate in the development of primitive man. In the later stages, however, the differentiation of man from the rest of the animals showed itself most clearly "in the use of the reasoning, intellectual powers of inhibition." Man had reached a stage where in evolution he was no longer dependent upon the guidance of instinct and automatic learned responses but was capable of making and carrying out choices on a basis of reason and intelligence. It was only by accepting this "inheritance" of conscious control and applying it to the body as well as the mind (to the whole psycho-physical self) that man could cope with the stresses of modern life and adapt himself to the changes that civilization imposed. It was man's refusal to go ahead on a conscious level and his attempts to solve his problems on a basis of subconscious control that were responsible for the perilous conditions of today. By continuing to rely on instinct instead of intelligence the race was no longer developing but was instead degenerating. "Stupidity in living" is the phrase Alexander used to describe contemporary behaviour.

"Inhibition" is a key concept in Alexander's thought. He used the concept in his earliest work. The term later had a negative connotation stamped on it by the Freudian school; but Alexander used it throughout his career because it said what he wanted to say more exactly than any other term. To Alexander, inhibition had a definite, operational meaning. It meant delaying the instantaneous response (learned or instinctive) to a stimulus until the response could be carried out in the way that was best suited to the well-being of the organism as a whole. Sir Charles Sherrington in *The Integrative Action of the Nervous System* (1906) had given currency to the term as the reciprocal of excitation in the organization of posture and movement. (He later extended the term to include "negative attention" on the psychological level.) Alexander quoted with approval Sherrington's statement:

> I may seem to stress the preoccupation of the brain with muscle. Can we stress too much that preoccupation when any path we trace in the brain leads directly or indirectly to muscle? The brain seems a thoroughfare for nerve action passing on its way to the motor animal. It has been remarked that Life's aim is an act not a thought. Today the dictum must be modified to admit that, often, to refrain from an act is no less an act than to commit one, because inhibition is co-equally with excitation a nervous activity [*The Universal Constant in Living*, p. 110].

There is an implied dualism in Sherrington's treatment of inhibition which is not to be found in Alexander's. To Alexander inhibition was not coequal with excitation: it came first. It is the fundamental process, conscious or unconscious, by which the integrity of the organism is maintained while a particular response is being carried out, or not carried out, as the case may be. It is the failure of inhibition that more than anything else is responsible for the dangerous state of the world. Restoring inhibition so that it can perform its integrative function on a conscious level should be the primary aim of education.

Some people have tried to dispense with inhibition in their explanations of the Technique, or to bring it in as an afterthought.

Pupils are asked to say over the directive orders to themselves while the instructor by manipulation gives them the "correct" experience that goes with the orders. Once the experience and order have been linked, they are substituted for the old stimulus–response pattern. This procedure, whether it succeeds or not, is not the Alexander Technique, but a form of classical conditioning. F. M. said on many occasions that his technique rested on inhibition as its base. A pupil who understands the principle of inhibition can learn the Technique in a relatively short time, he said. Without it he will be learning something quite different.

Though Alexander sometimes used inhibition as if it were a synonym of reason and intelligence, he did not consider it an exclusively human attribute. Animals, he said, showed it in the natural state. A wild cat stalking its prey, for example, "inhibits the desire to spring prematurely and controls to a deliberate end its eagerness for the instant gratification of a natural appetite." In primitive man the power of inhibition increased side by side with the growth of intelligence.

Believing that the fundamental problem of education—failure to move ahead onto a fully conscious plane—had to be solved first, Alexander had no use for partial solutions. In particular, he deplored methods of education and therapy that aimed at controlling and using, for whatever purpose, the "subconscious self," as if it were some kind of hidden entity subject to the force of suggestion or autosuggestion. He had no belief in or respect for "faith cures," considered hypnotism degrading, and anticipated Barber and others in denying that anything more can be accomplished in a trance than out of it. In *Man's Supreme Inheritance* Alexander does not give an exact definition of "subconscious self," but he clearly means by it not a hidden entity (which would destroy the unity of the organism), but a complex set of habits that operate automatically below the conscious level and that are the result of either instinct or prior learning.

Of the three factors that determine behaviour—heredity, imitation and learning (training)—Alexander considered only the last two to be significant. He dismissed heredity as negligible. "In the vast majority of cases," he said, "it can be practically eradicated." He believed in individual differences but not that one individual was innately superior or inferior to another; and he had no use for intelligence tests or other devices for putting people into categories. There were, of course, limits to the development of a particular child, but they were wide, and "within those limits our capacity for good and evil is very great."

Imitation is a powerful influence on development and one that is seldom taken into consideration. A child will imitate not only "our tricks of manner and speech" but also "our carriage of the body, our performance of muscular acts, even our very manner of breathing." "How many parents," he goes on to say, "attempt to put a right model before their children? How many learn to eradicate their own defects of poise and carriage, so that they may be better examples to the child? How many in choosing a nurse will take the trouble to select a girl whom they would like their children to imitate?" The reason, he says, that most parents cannot choose a girl "who is a good specimen of humanity" is that they are "sublimely unconscious of their own crookedness and defects." The principle extends into the primary and secondary schools where far too often teachers who are physically unfit are not only setting bad examples to their students but actually directing them in physical exercises.

Training, the other force that moulds the behaviour of child and adult, can also be used for good or ill. It was mostly used for ill, in Alexander's view. Even in infancy a child can learn bad food habits (sugar, which was commonly added to the milk, "debauched" the sense of taste) and the habit of crying to get what it wants—habits that later on lead to serious health and behaviour problems. The schools, however, are the worst offenders. He had already spoken in his pamphlets on respiration about the bad effect on posture and breathing of sitting long hours at a schoolroom desk. Worse than these were the exaggerated fear responses inculcated into the child by the rigid methods of discipline; the stunting of intelligence and free inquiry; and the habit of accepting without question whatever rules and precepts have been handed down from the past. "Why should not the child's powers of intelligence be trained? Why should they be stunted by forcing him to accept the preconceived ideas and traditions which have been handed down from generation to generation, without examination, without reason, without inquiry as to their truth or origin. The human mind of today is suffering partial paralysis by this method of forcing these unreasoned and antiquated principles upon the young and plastic intelligence." The situation would change, Alexander said, once it was realized that the race has progressed beyond the point where "right habits" can be drilled into children "until they have become sub-conscious and passed from the region of intelligent guidance." We are born with the potential for making free choices on the basis of reason and intelligence, and our training should be directed toward the realization of this potential. "I look for a time," he said, "when the child shall be so taught and trained that whatever the circumstance which shall later surround it, it will without effort be enabled to live its life in the enjoyment of perfect health, physical and mental."

Alexander thought the future salvation of the race lay in the education of the children. There was no reason, however, for the individual to wait for wholesale educational reform before making a change himself. Fortunately, habits that operated subconsciously to the enslavement of man could be raised to the conscious level and be made subject to intelligent control. A conscious habit works automatically just as an unconscious habit does, but it is plastic and subject to change and hence is the servant rather than the master of man. A habit need never be fixed. "It is merely a series of orders which will be carried out until countermanded."

Alexander's theories were not arrived at *a priori* by pure reasoning. They were derived from his own experience in establishing a degree of conscious control over his own stereotyped behaviour and in teaching his pupils to establish a similar control over theirs. In spite of the sweeping nature of his thesis, he presented it as a scientific hypothesis derived from empirical data. In his argument he is continually passing back and forth from theory to practice. He states explicitly that he is avoiding any "dogma" and that he is willing to "accept amendments" or even to alter one or another of his premises if new evidence should cause him to do so. A reader is apt to lose sight of the empirical nature of Alexander's argument and to accept or reject his conclusions according to the appeal they make to his own predilections. Many readers were attracted by Alexander's positive, optimistic thesis that man has by inheritance a mechanism that enables him to control his own destiny, free from the determinism of heredity and environment. Having accepted the thesis, they fre-

quently went on either to have lessons in the Technique or try to
practice "conscious control" on their own. Others were repelled by
the thesis, which they considered philosophical and speculative
rather than scientific, and rejected the therapeutic claim contemp-
tuously and without investigation.

Man's Supreme Inheritance in its first version ran to only 140 pages
(Alexander referred to it as a brochure). It was followed by *Conscious
Control* (1912), in which he applied his theories to the "acts of everyday life," attempting to show by concrete instances that the race was
in fact degenerating and that subconscious guidance was incapable
of reversing the trend. In the selection and organization of the material and the style in which it is presented the two books reflect
Alexander's lack of academic background, a lack that undoubtedly
worked against the acceptance of his work by the scientific commu-
nity. On the other hand, though they do not have the precision and
coherence (and technical jargon) of sophisticated scientific writing,
both books, but especially the first, have the authenticity and excitement of something important that is being said for the first time. With
them Alexander succeeded in what he set out to do; he brought his
work to the attention of the intelligent, reading public. The books
received favourable reviews in the lay press, and Alexander's reputation expanded far beyond the acting profession. Having lessons in
the Alexander Technique became a fashionable thing to do in certain circles, and from this time on a succession of wealthy and titled
individuals, beginning with the Earl of Lytton, began coming to him
for lessons. This turn of events distressed some of his followers, who
felt that he was unduly affected by his success. "Nothing can take away
the real greatness of his work," wrote Louise Morgan in 1954, ". . . but
he let his head be turned. . . . If he had stayed in Australia, and taught
ordinary people in a humble way instead of famous actors and
industrial giants and lords and ladies, he would have in the end been
a world figure, a benefactor of mankind. . . ." I do not agree. In spite
of his naïve pleasure in name-dropping and his high fees, he had
great singleness of purpose. The lords and ladies helped to establish
him as an accepted figure in London. It was only in that way, he
believed, that he could establish the principle he had discovered.

The person who probably did the most to establish Alexander
in London was Ethel M. Webb, who served for many years as his

secretary and receptionist and mediated between him and the public. Miss Webb, who was somewhat older than F. M., belonged to a well-connected Unitarian family. She was a woman of character and breeding with a good education in literature and music and might have had a career as a pianist if her health had permitted. She had a great deal of trouble with her back, however, and did not have the strength to perform professionally. Her interest was aroused by *Man's Supreme Inheritance*, which had been favourably reviewed by William Archer in *The Morning Leader*, and she arranged to have lessons in the Technique. The marked improvement in her health that followed convinced her of the revolutionary importance of Alexander's discovery, and she determined to devote the rest of her life to gaining acceptance for the Alexander principle.

Miss Webb read widely in educational theory and made an intensive study of the writings of John Dewey. In 1913, thinking that there might be a connection for education between Alexander's work and the work of Maria Montessori, she went to Rome to study at the Montessori school. There she met two other women who were to play important parts in the propagation of Alexander's ideas: Irene Tasker, who had graduated from Cambridge and had taken up teaching as a profession, and Margaret Naumburg from New York, who had studied with John Dewey at Columbia and who later founded the Walden School. Miss Tasker and Miss Naumburg were much interested in Miss Webb's account of Alexander and went to London for lessons in the Technique. Both were strongly impressed by the lessons. Miss Naumburg felt that it was very important that Alexander and Dewey should meet. When the war broke out in 1914, she invited Alexander to come to New York, promising to send him as many pupils as he wanted.

5

Constructive Conscious Control
of the Individual

It may be said that Mr. Alexander treats the body as Freud does the mind. The work of the two men seems to me to be supplementary, and I am not sure that Alexander's is not more fundamental.

Horace M. Kallen

"NON-END-GAINING" is a basic principle of the Alexander Technique. As the Alexander brothers applied the principle, it often seemed to mean: wait; stick to the means-whereby; the right solution to the problem will emerge. Margaret Naumburg's invitation was a case in point. F. M. told me that in 1914 he was just beginning to find a new way of using his hands in teaching. By applying the inhibitory control (which had proved so effective in breathing and speaking) to the use of his hands he was learning to make changes in a pupil that were different from ordinary manipulation or postural adjustment. (F. M. worked directly with the reflexes where an osteopath corrected lesions, Bernard Shaw said.) When the war broke out, the number of his pupils was drastically reduced and with it the opportunity to perfect the newly discovered use of his hands. The invitation to teach in New York solved the problem.

F. M. landed in New York late in 1914. Ethel Webb, who had friends at Columbia University, came over at the same time. A. R. followed a few months later. Margaret Naumburg kept her promise about pupils, and the Technique was soon well known at Columbia. Whole families came for lessons, the Dewey family among them. In 1916 Dewey himself was introduced to the Technique and began having lessons, a practice that he continued at intervals throughout his life. In that same year Irene Tasker accepted an invitation to teach at the newly founded Walden School and enrolled as a graduate student at Columbia in order to study with Dewey. She also continued to study the Alexander Technique and became F. M.'s assistant in 1918, working primarily with children. London was not neglected during this period. F. M. went back and forth to England, but until 1924 he spent at least four months of every year in the United States.

In January 1918, Dutton brought out a new American edition of *Man's Supreme Inheritance*, with an introduction by John Dewey. It was expanded to include *Conscious Control*. The original text of both books remained largely unchanged, but some new material was added.

In a chapter on the "crisis of 1914," Alexander blamed the outbreak of war on the failure of civilized nations to move from a subconscious to a conscious principle of behaviour. He singled out Germany for the brunt of the blame because her people had accepted the doctrine of "might is right" without questioning it and had hypnotized themselves into thinking they were destined to dominate the world. He found the cause for Germany's "self-hypnosis" in the combination of commercial industry and militarism. "One of the greatest features connected with the former," he said, "was the extraordinary development of machinery, which demanded for its successful pursuance that the individual should be subjected to the most harmful systems of automatic training. The standardized parts of the machine made demands which tended to stereotype the human machine. . . . The power to continue work under such conditions depended upon a process of deterioration in the individual. He was slowly but surely being robbed of the possibility of development."

Germany, Alexander thought, was an extreme case of the evils which he deplored in rigid, authoritarian systems of education. In America, however, he had seen some of the newer schools of "free expression." In an expanded chapter on education he condemned these schools in stronger terms than those he had applied to traditional schools. The latter, he said, "with their definite prohibitions and their exact instructions were less harmful than the extremes of the modern school that would base their scheme of education upon a child's instinctive reactions," which they assumed to be reliable—an assumption, Alexander said, that was "demonstrably fallacious."

Dewey thought Alexander "must have made the acquaintance of an extremely rare type of 'self-expressive' school." He added, however, that "all interested in educational reform may well remember that freedom of physical action and free expression of emotion are means, not ends, and that as means they are justified only in so far as they are used as conditions for developing power of intelligence."

The revised edition of *Man's Supreme Inheritance* was the most widely read of Alexander's books. Most of the reviews were highly favourable. R. M. Hodge in the *New York Times Book Review*, Horace M. Kallen in the *Dial*, and James Harvey Robinson in the *Atlantic Monthly* all found the book readable and inspiring. What they particularly liked was Alexander's appeal to reason and intelligence; his rejection of subconscious guidance and control; the reverence in which he held the human body; and his belief in human potential for constructive change.

The longest and most influential of the reviews was Robinson's eight-page article, "The Philosopher's Stone." Robinson saw in Alexander's educational methods an exhilarating hope for the future: "I think his ability to straighten out adults and give them new energy and courage is very important, but by no means as important as the possible application of his theories in the field of education, by which it seems as if it might be possible to raise the whole race to a far higher plane than it now occupies." Robinson was greatly impressed by Alexander's insistence on mind-body unity and his belief that political and social reforms could not be made practical as long as the men who had to carry them out "remained dependent on subconscious guidance."

It is significant that Hodge, Kallen and Robinson had all had lessons in the Technique, which Hodge said was "incommunicable on paper." Robinson tried to solve the problem (as Aldous Huxley did later) by giving a detailed description of an actual lesson. The problem of how to use words to convey sensory experience to someone who has not had the experience before continued to plague Alexander and all who have written about the Technique since, and it has not yet been solved. Reviewers who had not had lessons usually misrepresented Alexander's thesis or missed it altogether. Randolph Bourne ("R. B."), who reviewed *Man's Supreme Inheritance* for the *New Republic*, angered Dewey by stating that Alexander "seems to have demonstrated" not a principle, but "that he possesses a rare physiological intuition and technique of re-educating the body." Bourne described the Technique as "apparently a kind of reversed psychoanalysis, unwinding the psychic knots by getting control of the physical end-organs." (The comparison of Alexander with Freud was also made by Kallen and Robinson.) Dewey would have none of this, rejecting with contempt Bourne's assumption that Alexander had some "personal intuition or quasi-magical personal knack" instead of a basic principle of psycho-physical unity. In retrospect Dewey seems unduly severe to Bourne, who, after all, was merely suggesting that Alexander's technique could profitably be considered apart from his philosophy. Bourne thought mankind was "a pitiful and struggling army" and despaired of teaching them anything like intelligent conscious control.

The success of *Man's Supreme Inheritance* and the prestige of the *Atlantic Monthly* spread the knowledge of the Alexander Technique beyond the confines of the Columbia campus and New York City. In 1920 the Alexander brothers were invited to Boston by Miss Caroline Atkinson and Mrs. Ernest Amory Codman, who had read "The Philosopher's Stone" in the *Atlantic* and gone to New York to find out whether Robinson's appraisal of the Technique was warranted. From then until 1924 one or both of the brothers came regularly to Boston whenever they were in this country and gave lessons either at Miss Atkinson's home in Brookline or the home of Dr. and Mrs. Codman on Beacon Street. This was the best kind of sponsorship for Boston. Miss Atkinson's father was one of the founders of the Boston Symphony; Mrs. Codman was a Bowditch; and Dr. Codman, who had an appointment at the Massachusetts General Hospital, was a pioneer in the study of X-rays and an international authority on the shoulder. The Technique was thus given a stamp of respectability which made it socially and medically acceptable in Boston and Cambridge. As in New York, whole families came in for lessons, the children sometimes reluctantly at their parents' insistence. Mrs. Richard G. Wadsworth, a younger sister of Miss Atkinson, remembered a Christmas party at which two of the children created a great deal of merriment by dressing up like the Alexander brothers and giving everyone a lesson. With the exception of Miss Atkinson's personal physician, Dr. Millard Smith, Boston doctors did not often refer patients to the Alexanders, though when asked if it would be all right to have lessons they would usually say, "They can't do you any harm." Dr. Codman did not have lessons himself but was happy for his wife to do so, since after beginning them she was able to resume mountain climbing, which she had given up because of arthritis. The Alexanders did not help matters by their intransigent attitude. At a reception which was given for them by the Codmans, and to which a large number of prominent doctors and their wives were invited, F. M. announced that the practice of medicine was much more advanced in England than in America. A. R. said that psychoanalysis was cultish and probably did more harm than good. At a time when Harvard University was the bastion of Freudian orthodoxy, such an opinion could not win many friends in Boston. People continued to have lessons, however, and to report back enthusiastically to their doctors. At the Massachusetts General Hospital the file on the Alexander Technique was said to be a foot and a half thick.

Alexander was frequently accused by the medical profession of claiming to cure disease (see Chapter 10). He always denied the charge. What he claimed was that the use of the Technique raised the general level of health and that the results in some of the cases he had treated had astonished him (*Man's Supreme Inheritance*, p. 234). These included cases of paralysis, tuberculosis, asthma, "incipient appendicitis" and colitis. To claim that a person's health improved after lessons while denying that the Technique was presented as a cure for disease may seem like a quibble over words, but I do not believe it was. There is a real difference between a "cure" that is achieved by a remedy specifically designed to treat disease, and a general improvement in health which brings with it the disappearance of particular disease symptoms. The "cures" were significant because they illustrated a general principle. Alexander promised his pupils that if they learned the Technique old motor habits would be broken up and "an improved efficiency" would "follow as a matter of course." This would bring with it an increased resistance to infectious diseases and "an ability to check the formation of any bad, incipient muscular or mental habit." In other words, the Technique was not curative but preventive.

If Alexander would not promise quick and easy cures, there were others who would, and they were much more successful than he in reaching the public. Emile Coué (1857–1926) achieved a great vogue at this time in both England and America with his method of auto-suggestion, or positive thinking ("Day by day in every way I am getting better and better"). In public demonstrations Coué frequently got lame men to walk and dumb men to speak. He improved the voices of aging singers, and once, in the presence of one hundred physicians, he cured thirty neurasthenics. In January 1923, Coué and Alexander arrived in New York on the same boat. While reporters and photographers milled around the former, the latter slipped quietly down the gangplank unobserved by the press. The discrepancy did not pass unnoticed, however. Dewey described the incident for the *New Republic* (January 24, 1923) in a piece entitled "A Sick World." "The contrast between the receptions of the two men," Dewey wrote, "affords a fair measure of our preference for a seemingly cheap and easy way of dealing with symptoms, of our wish to be cured rather than to be well."

Dewey said that he did not want to sound unsympathetic to anyone who had experienced a cure or to begrudge him the relief that he felt he had obtained from his symptoms. "But all cheap short cuts," he went on, "which avoid recognition of basic causes have to be paid for at great cost. The greatest cost is that palliative and remedial measures put off the day in which fundamental causal factors are faced and constructive action undertaken. They [sc. 'cures'] perpetuate the domination of life by reverie, magic, superficiality, and evasion; they perpetuate, that is, the sickness of the world. . . . Only education and re-education into normal conditions of growth accomplishes anything positive and enduring. . . . Dependence on cures retards, hampers and confuses. Partial and superficial science, physiological and psychological, carried into immediate execution, is the greatest enemy of genuine and effective science. It substitutes error for ignorance, false conceit for the possibility of learning. Suggestions to the subconscious have the advantage of neither the animal nor the human method of control. They are a hopeless mixture."

Couéism, Dewey said, though "dressed up in the latest fashion of the day was as old as the cave-man." The principle of conscious control, which Alexander advocated, was something altogether different. It was not curative, or palliative, or cheap and easy. It called for moral and intellectual commitment from the pupil. In return, it gave him a positive standard of health and the means of attaining it.

In the spring of 1923 both F. M. and A. R. Alexander were in Boston, teaching at Miss Atkinson's apartment on Brimmer Street overlooking the Charles River. John Dewey had come up from New York for a course of lessons. F. M. was hurrying to complete his new book, *Constructive Conscious Control of the Individual.* Dewey read it critically, made suggestions for revision, and wrote an introduction for it. Dutton brought it out in May, just after F. M. returned to England, and there was a second printing in November.

One reason for hurrying the publication was the recent appearance of a book called *Invisible Exercise: Seven Studies in Self-Command with Practical Suggestions and Drills* (Dutton, 1922), by Gerald Stanley Lee. *Invisible Exercise* was the first of a long series of books and articles that were inspired directly or indirectly by Alexander's teaching, but that debased the principle by leaving out some essential feature, usually inhibition, so that the Technique emerged as a set of physical, mental or spiritual exercises.

Gerald Stanley Lee (1862–1944) was an ordained minister in the Congregational Church, a writer of popular books on religious subjects, and a Lecturer on Literature and the Arts at Smith College. He and his wife, Jennette Barbour Lee (1867–1951) studied with Alexander in London for eighteen months immediately after the war. Alexander maintained that the Lees never did understand the Technique. They returned from London greatly improved in health, however, and Lee in his next book (*The Ghost in the White House,* Dutton, 1920) hailed Alexander as a genius in whose brain and hands could be found the skill needed to save civilization. Like James Harvey Robinson, Lee compared F. M. to a sculptor who "takes you in his hands—his very powerful sensitive hands and begins—quite literally begins reshaping you like Phidias." So enthusiastic was Lee about the Technique that he wanted to send "the whole US Senate, better yet, everyone in the USA to be Alexandered." This being impractical, Lee thought the next best thing would be to put the ideas into a popular book that everyone could understand. He didn't think this would be hard to do, since Alexander's principles (as distinct from the use of his hands) were the same ones that he himself had held for a long time.

When *Invisible Exercise* came out two years later, Lee had forgotten that he owed Alexander anything. He makes no mention of him, nor does he refer to the lessons in London. Instead, he tells of how he went up into the hills (the slopes of Mount Tom behind Northampton) and how the whole thing came to him like a mystical experience. By a sudden insight he realized that instead of tensing his neck against the cold he could relax it and stretch his upper back and that this would give him increased control over everything else. From this experience he worked out, he said, a system of "orders" to his neck to relax, his head to go forward and up, to lengthen and widen his back. The orders led him to invent a number of "drills"—a drill for walking, a drill for standing, a drill for lying down with two books under his head, and a drill for sitting in a chair with his hands on the back of another chair and pulling on it to widen his back.

All of the orders and drills that Lee claimed to have invented had been used routinely by Alexander in the lessons he gave Lee in London. Lee took them and made exercises out of them by leaving out the principles of inhibition and sensory unreliability. By background and training Lee was unable to accept the unity of the organism. After dividing the self into body and mind he went on to divide the mind into conscious and subconscious. As he explained in a later book (*Rest Working*, 1926) the way to learn a new habit (like relaxing the neck) was to do it as an exercise, consciously at first until it could be "left in charge" of the subconscious. The conscious mind could then go off and "put through some new and fascinating experience," confident that the subconscious mind would take care of the order to the neck to relax.

Incensed at this travesty of his technique, Alexander threatened the publishers (ironically they were the same as his) with legal action unless they withdrew Lee's book. Without waiting for this to happen, he decided that he must prove to the public there was something more to his technique than "invisible exercises." Accordingly, he wrote out a long description of what he did with a pupil in a lesson. He chose the hands-behind-the-chair procedure (which he had been using, he said, since 1910) and went through it step by step, explaining fully what part the teacher played and what the pupil, what the "orders" meant and how they were related to the manipulation of the teacher. Where Lee had been content with half a page of description, Alexander used sixteen. Satisfied that the account was accurate and complete, he looked for a way of having it patented. Since this was not practicable, he incorporated it into his new book, where it was protected by copyright.

Alexander also hoped that by giving a full account of his "technical manoeuvres and evolutions" he would answer the objections that some readers of *Man's Supreme Inheritance* had made, "that you give us enough to make us interested in your theory and just lead us to the point where we realize we must come to you for lessons." He denied that his books had been designed in any way as a come-on. His aim in writing them was to alert the world to the degenerative effect that civilization was making on the human organism and to outline the steps that must be taken to reverse the process. Besides the detailed account of a lesson, he described three of his devices for proving to a pupil that his senses deceived him: he asked him 1) to move his head without his shoulders; 2) to open his mouth without tilting his head back; 3) to turn out his toes without shifting his heels first. Most people, he said, are unable to do any of these, but their kinaesthesia is so poorly developed that they are not aware of it.

The greater part of *Constructive Conscious Control* is given over to instances showing the futility of relying on end-gaining cures when the race can be saved only by adopting a means-whereby principle of prevention. Modern man, he said, is like someone who is "lost in the bush; who, becoming oblivious of these signs which, if he were not emotionally disturbed, could not escape his observation, wanders round and round in a circle, and after a long and sad experience finds himself back at the place from which he started." All of our fashionable cures are merely reactions to other cures with which we have become disillusioned. We cannot break out of this circle until we are willing to move up onto a plane of conscious control.

One of the examples he chose to show the degeneration of modern man was "mind wandering." In the savage state, mind wandering would be fatal and the individual without the ability to respond appropriately to a novel situation could not survive at all. The answer, Alexander repeats, is not concentration, but a general alertness. (In conversation he illustrated the point by another example from his Australian experience: an amateur who went hunting in the bush looked for game by concentrating his attention first on one spot and then on another. But while he was concentrating, the bird would rise somewhere else and he would miss it. The true hunter, on the other hand, took in the whole landscape with his gaze and was prepared for whatever happened wherever it happened.)

Closely connected with mind wandering is the increasing loss of memory evidenced by the prevalence of "memory systems" and courses of "mental training." All of these systems and courses, Alexander said, were based on an end-gaining principle and were bound to fail. They start out by dividing the organism into mind and body, then proceed to treat what they call the mind separately, ignoring the psycho-physical functioning that is present when the memory trace is formed. Everything that is remembered, Alexander pointed out, has to come to us through one or the other of the senses. The strength of a memory trace "depends upon certain psycho-physical processes concerned with registering impressions, and the effectiveness of these processes in their turn upon the general psycho-physical condition, and especially upon the standard of sensory appreciation present in the particular case." The decay of memory, then, is directly related to the lowering standard of sensory appreciation.

The fact that remarkable feats of memory are still being reported did not, Alexander maintained, invalidate his thesis. These feats were almost always confined to a single sphere and were matched by failures elsewhere. As a case in point he described a pupil of his, a young man whose "abnormality" it was to glance over a railway timetable, memorize the whole list, and be able three months later to recall any item he was asked for. This same young man, however, continually left his umbrella on the bus and when he went shopping would forget what he went for and return without it. At this point Alexander stops to warn against placing an exaggerated value upon specialized intelligence. "Judgement must always be made," he goes on to say, "upon the human creature's intelligent activities on a general basis in the process of living and all-round usefulness."

Among his examples of end-gaining cures, Alexander cited psychoanalysis, which he must have become aware of after the new edition of *Man's Supreme Inheritance* came out and the reviewers had compared his work to Freud's. The comparison could not have pleased Alexander. He had only a superficial (if any) acquaintance with psychoanalytic literature, but he was sure that it dealt with effects rather than causes. Though analysis might rid the patient of a particular phobia, Alexander did not see how it could correct his "debauched kinaesthesia" and restore a reliable sensory appreciation. "The psycho-physical condition which permitted the establishment of the first phobia will permit the establishment of another. All that is needed is the stimulus" (*Constructive Conscious Control*, p. 92). Alexander was fond of quoting the Bible. One of his favourite passages was the parable of the unclean spirit: "When the unclean spirit is gone out of a man, he walketh through dry places, seeking rest; and finding none, he saith, I will return unto my house whence I came out. And when he cometh, he findeth it swept and garnished. Then goeth he, and taketh to him seven other spirits more wicked than himself; and they enter in, and dwell there: and the last state of that man is worse than the first" (Luke 11:24–26).

In a long chapter titled "Unduly Excited Fear Reflexes" Alexander gives his own analysis of the causes of abnormal behaviour and his prescription for change. What the growing child should have, he says, is a balanced state in which inhibition and volition develop equally. What one commonly sees, however, is an imbalance: "In certain spheres there has been a harmful and exaggerated development of the inhibitory processes, often causing virtues to become almost vices, whilst in other spheres there has been a correspondingly harmful lack." The child starts his school career with "a poor equipment on the inhibitory side" and school tends to unbalance him further until at adolescence unduly excited fear reflexes are usually present in some degree. Pupils at their lessons show "more or less uncontrolled emotions" as they try to carry out new instructions correctly. "Watch the fixed expression of these pupils . . . and their tendency to hold the breath by assuming a harmful posture and exerting an exaggerated strain such as they would employ in performing strenuous 'physical' acts." Learning to these students means doing "correctly" whatever the teacher insists on having done. The imperfectly coordinated student, however, cannot do anything "correctly" at the start; he is bound to have failures no matter how hard he tries. Under the present end-gaining system of learning, failure brings with it strong emotional reactions and a pattern of anxiety that is never gotten rid of, even after the activity has been learned. "Every unsuccessful 'try' not only reinforces the pupil's old wrong psycho-physical habits associated with his conception of a particular act, but involves at the same time new emotional experiences of discourage-ment, worry, fear, and anxiety." If a means-whereby principle were used in teaching, Alexander said, the pupil would not be asked to perform an act until he was in such a state of coordination that he could perform it easily. An occasional failure would not then be charged with any emotion but would merely add to the pupil's know-ledge of his own responses.

Since the school experience is a paradigm of learning situations outside of school and since the general standard of sensory judge-ment is so poor, there should be nothing surprising about the preva-lence of bad habits like alcoholism and other perverted forms of sensory satisfaction including "sensory satisfaction through actual pain." Alexander, though he never discusses the topic of sex expli-citly, is clearly thinking of it when he says that "fundamental desires and needs must be satisfied" even though the attempt to satisfy them "leads many individuals to indulge in abuse and excess," which are always associated with abnormality. The way to deal with abnormal behaviour, Alexander said, was not by denying the individual any means for satisfying his desires but by getting rid of the conditions that were responsible for the abnormality and restoring "the reliable sensory appreciation which ensures the maintenance of normality in our desires and needs."

The last chapter in the book is entitled "Sensory Appreciation in its Relation to Happiness." Happiness is defined as "doing well something that interests you." It can be seen at its clearest in a healthy child at play whose pleasure resides in the satisfaction of making something work. This satisfaction, Alexander says, can be established even more strongly when the mechanism that is made to work is the child's own. Here he describes vividly the change in facial expression and the look of pleasure that a child shows when he suddenly dis-covers in a lesson that he can do easily and in a coordinated manner something he has always done awkwardly before, realizing, for example, that he can in this way improve his skill in games. "It is a happiness," Alexander said, "which increases with psycho-physical improvement." In marked contrast is the unhappiness shown by most adults as they approach middle age and realize that they are not improving in themselves but deteriorating. Success is essential to happiness in everyone. When happiness cannot be obtained in the ordinary way, in the satisfaction of using oneself optimally in the routine of everyday life, a person will begin pursuing specific pleasures. People unfortunately have been taught to make the routine activities of daily living automatic and as far as possible unconscious. This leads to a condition of stagnation and the harmful demand for specific excitements and stimulations, none of which can possibly produce real happiness. Such happiness can only be obtained by restoring to a person his own sensory standard so that he can gradually re-establish a pattern of growth and self-satisfaction that will carry him beyond middle age and into old age. Happiness, then, consists in the sensory satisfaction that comes with an increase of self-knowledge and control. This satisfaction extends to all aspects of living (including, of course, the sexual).

6

The Use of the Self

It is difficult to conceive anything more scientifically bigoted than to postulate that all possible experience conforms to the same type as that with which we are already familiar in everyday experience.
P. W. Bridgman, *The Logic of Modern Physics*

ALEXANDER ALWAYS considered *Constructive Conscious Control* his most important book. It was more ambitiously planned than any of the others; the examples and the language were carefully chosen; and it had the benefit of Dewey's advice. It did not succeed with either the critics or the public, however. For the public the elaborate care with which it was written took away some of the readability—the freshness and the excitement of discovery that the earlier book conveyed—and it did not break new ground or add substantially to the argument. The critics, who were used to judging a theory by how well it fitted into the system of ideas with which they were already familiar, were confused because Alexander was applying a principle of mind-body unity, to which they all paid lip service, not to philosophy, but to the sphere of everyday living, where they were not prepared to follow him. To judge the validity of the principle it would have been necessary to have lessons in the Technique or at least to have a demonstration of it. Having lessons, however, might have forced them to revise some of their deeply held ideas; like the professor of philosophy at the University of Padua who refused to look through Galileo's telescope, they preferred to reject the book on intellectual grounds.

After the failure of *Constructive Conscious Control* to establish the Technique on a firmer basis in education and medicine, Dewey undertook to find foundation support for a scientific investigation of the Technique. He succeeded in obtaining a commitment from the Rockefeller Foundation, but Alexander set up so many requirements for his own participation that the project fell through. This was a great disappointment for Dewey, and the personal relations between the two became and remained strained, though Dewey continued to support Alexander's work and to have lessons in the Technique from his brother. In defence of Alexander's reluctance to sanction the proposed investigation it should be said that he had no confidence in the validity of the methods that would be employed in testing the results of the study and was unwilling to allow the future of the Technique to depend on the outcome of an investigation over which he had no control. At that stage in the development of the Technique he may have been right.

What Alexander did consent to do was to write a detailed account of the self-observations and experiments that had led up to the discovery and perfection of his technique. "The Evolution of a Technique" is the first chapter of Alexander's next book, *The Use of the Self* (1932). The chapter is an exemplar of all the major steps that, according to Dewey, are characteristic of a scientific inquiry. (Dewey said that in this account anyone who does not "identify science with a parade of technical vocabulary will find the essentials of scientific method.") It starts out with a concrete problem (loss of voice) and describes: 1) the failure to solve it by orthodox means; 2) the design of a method for making controlled observations and collecting data; 3) the use of instruments (mirrors) for correcting and supplementing sense data obtained in the inquiry; 4) the unexpected discovery that there was a regular sequence of events that preceded the loss of voice; 5) the introduction of a change in the sequence in order to observe what other changes would (or would not) follow; 6) the setting up and testing of new hypotheses to account for the new facts; 7) the construction of a generalised theory to account for both the original observations and the new experimental data; 8) the discovery that the new theory could explain additional facts and solve additional problems besides those for which it was set up. Alexander's final conclusion, that the way the organism is used determines the way it functions—"use determines functioning" (which might be called "Alexander's law")—can be demonstrated so anyone who wishes can know it, Dewey said, "through the series of experiences which he himself has. The genuinely scientific character of Mr. Alexander's teaching can be safely rested on this fact alone."

The Use of the Self shows an advance in Alexander's thinking about the Technique in two key concepts, "use," which is brought into the title of the book, and "primary control."

In his earlier books Alexander speaks of the use of the psycho-physical organism, the use of the respiratory mechanisms, etc. In *The Use of the Self* he makes an abstract noun of the term, commensurate with "heredity" and "environment". Behavioural scientists usually feel that when they have accounted for genetic factors and environmental influences (including learning) they have said all there is to be said about the individual and that if all genetic and environmental factors were known it would be possible to predict behaviour. There is a third factor, however: the characteristic way the person uses himself in everything he does. Until this factor is known, no prediction can be made. It would be like predicting the life of a new piece of machinery without knowing how efficiently it is going to be operated. The term "use" covers the total pattern that characterizes a person's responses to stimuli. Use is subject to a variety of influences from without and within the organism. Unlike heredity and previous experience, use can be brought under conscious control and redirected to enlarge the individual's potential for creative development.

In his early treatise "Re-education of the Kinaesthetic Systems," Alexander used the term "position of mechanical advantage" to describe a specific position in which the pupil is placed by the teacher and from which "by the mental rehearsal of orders he can insure the posture specifically correct for himself" (*Man's Supreme Inheritance*, 1910, p. 193). It is a position in which breathing and other psycho-physical activities are facilitated. The term disappears from Alexander's writings after 1923. Though he continued to put pupils into such positions I never heard him use the terms "position" or "posture," and he advised me in 1946 to avoid the word "posture" in writing about the Technique.

In *The Use of the Self*, the term "position of mechanical advantage" is replaced by "primary control," a different concept altogether. Alexander defines it as a control that "depends upon a certain use of the head and neck in relation to the rest of the body." The primary control "governs the working of all the mechanisms and so renders the control of the complex human organism comparatively simple" (pp. 59–60). Alexander apparently had the idea of a primary control in the relation of the head to the neck at least as early as 1912. In *Conscious Control* (reprinted in the 1918 edition of *Man's Supreme Inheritance*) he gives as the first in the series of directive orders: "neck to relax, head forward and up." The idea does not seem to have crystallized, however, until after some of his medical friends had called his attention to the work of Rudolph Magnus.

Rudolph Magnus (1873–1927), who was professor of pharmacology at the University of Utrecht, had a passionate interest in exploring the rôle played by physiological mechanisms in mental functions. In 1908 he went to England to study with Sir Charles Sherrington and to learn the surgical techniques he had developed for analysing the reflex behaviour of animals. By making an incision in the brain stem of an animal and cutting off the higher centres of voluntary control Sherrington had been able to study and describe a great many patterns of reflex behaviour and show how they were integrated by the nervous system. Magnus was struck by the central rôle played by the reflexes governing the position of the animal's head in relation to space and in relation to the rest of the body. At Utrecht he directed an elaborate investigation of the phenomenon. He and his colleagues published over three hundred scientific papers on the postural reflexes, culminating in the *Körperstellung*, a 715-page treatise on animal posture published in 1924. His work demonstrated that head–neck reflexes were the central mechanism in orienting the animal to his environment ("bringing space into the right position") both in maintaining a posture assumed for a particular purpose and in restoring the animal to the normal resting posture after the purpose had been fulfilled. It is through the mediation of head–neck reflexes that a "moving mouse impresses on [a] cat . . . an attitude, by which the cat is focused toward the mouse and made ready for movement. The only thing the cat has to do is decide: to jump or not to jump. All other things have been prepared beforehand reflexly under the influence of the mouse . . . " (*Animal Posture*, p. 345). If then the mouse retreats, the stimulus to the attitudinal reflex is removed and the other set of reflexes, the righting reflexes in which head–neck reflexes again play the dominant rôle, take over and the cat is restored to the normal position. "In this way," Magnus says, "all the senses of the body regain their precise relation to the outer world" (1930, p. 103).

The *Körperstellung* was not translated in Alexander's lifetime, but two of Magnus's papers were in English. His Croonian Lecture at Edinburgh, which was published in the *Proceedings of the Royal Society* (1925), and an article in the *Lancet* (September 11, 1926) had wide circulation in England. Doctors who were Alexander's pupils were immediately struck by the similarities between Alexander's teaching and the experiments of Magnus. In an important paper published in the *British Medical Journal* (December 25, 1926), Dr. Peter Macdonald (President of the Yorkshire Branch of the British Medical Association) called attention to Magnus's precept that "the whole mechanism of the body acts in such a way that the head leads and the body follows," and pointed out that Alexander in his teaching had anticipated some of the results that Magnus and his colleagues had arrived at through laboratory experiments.

Some doctors objected to the comparison of Alexander's primary control with the central control (*Zentralapparat*) of Magnus on the ground that Magnus was referring not to the relation of head to trunk but to the anatomical centre in the brainstem where the postural reflexes are integrated. This is a verbal quibble. Alexander did not claim to have discovered an anatomical centre; Magnus, on the other hand, did not rest his explanation on the location of the centre but on the function of the reflexes. The doctrine of a "primary control," whether or not it was the same control as the one demonstrated by Magnus, provided Alexander with a parsimonious explanation for his findings, and he continued to use it along with "inhibition" and "use" when talking or writing about his technique. The term was accepted by Dewey and by most of the medical men who wrote about the Technique in the twenties and thirties. In *Health and Education through Self-Mastery* (1933), the first book about the Technique not written by Alexander himself, Anthony M. Ludovici, whose information came from the *Körperstellung* itself rather than the two articles published in England, assembled a large number of passages from both Magnus and Sherrington to show the bearing of their work on Alexander's.

The autobiographical narrative makes up the first section of the *The Use of the Self*. Having described how he arrived at his principle of conscious direction and control, Alexander goes on to apply it to two concrete cases: a stutterer and a golfer who cannot keep his eye on the ball. Alexander worked a great deal with golfers as well as with stutterers and used illustrations from golf in all of his books. (Leo Stein, Gertrude's brother, once described the Alexander Technique as the principle of keeping your eye on the ball applied to everyday life.) The two cases illustrate the importance of re-education on a general rather than a specific basis. Both the golfer and the stutterer had tried many methods of cure but they were not able to overcome their reliance on feeling and their addiction to "end-gaining." They knew what to do (or not do), but when the stimulus was received neither of them knew how to inhibit his old tendency to make a vast increase of unnecessary tension in preparing for the response. The solution for both of them, as it had been for Alexander himself, was to establish a control in which inhibition of the old response maintained the organism in balance until the new response was established.

In the final chapter Alexander argues for the introduction of the Technique into the medical curriculum. If a young doctor understood the principle of the primary control, he said, he would possess an invaluable diagnostic tool, since he would be able to estimate how much a patient's faulty "use" of himself contributed to his disability, and could add to the effectiveness of his treatment for mental as well as physical conditions.

In an appendix to *The Use of the Self* Alexander referred to two important events in the history of the Technique: the establishment of the Alexander Trust Fund School and the organization of a training course for teachers.

In 1924 a child whose parents were in India was sent to Alexander for lessons. He was nervous and excitable and Alexander felt that he needed daily help in employing the new use of himself in his schoolwork. Other parents who were themselves having lessons asked for the same kind of help for their children, and a class was set up to provide academic instruction for them, "upon the principle," Alexander wrote, "that the end for which they are working is of minor importance as compared with the way they direct the use of themselves for the gaining of that end." The class was put in the charge of Irene Tasker, who had returned to London from the United States. She later had the assistance of Margaret Goldie, a graduate of the Froebel Institute, and for a year, of Majorie Barstow of Lincoln, Nebraska.

At this time Alexander had made no formal arrangements for training teachers. Besides his brother, A. R., he was assisted in his teaching by Ethel Webb, who also served as secretary and interviewed prospective pupils, and by Irene Tasker. All three had been recruited into teaching at various times as demand for lessons increased, and all had learned by the apprenticeship method. Now, however, it was felt important to place the training of teachers on a more formal basis. Teachers in training would have individual lessons and class work under the supervision of F. M. or A. R. The course would run for three years but after the students had "reached a given standard in the use of themselves," they would get practical experience teaching in the "little school." The prospectus that was sent out contained laudatory statements signed by seven doctors, two heads of schools, the principal of the Froebel Institute, Sir Lyndon Macassey, the Earl of Lytton and Professor John Dewey. In an "Open Letter to Intending Students," Alexander said that he had delayed starting a training course until he was convinced that there was sufficient demand for teachers, but that frequent requests were now coming in, especially from the fields of medicine and education. He added that for other professions—medicine, law or philosophy—students could take the course without their use of themselves coming into question, but that students would not be allowed to graduate from his course and go out to teach others until their own standard of use had reached a satisfactory level.

The course began in February 1931, with seven students enrolled, the number gradually increasing to twelve. An account of the early days in the training course can be found in Lulie Westfeldt's *F. Matthias Alexander: The Man and his Work* (1964). Lulie Westfeldt, who later taught the Technique in New York, had been crippled by polio at the age of seven. A series of operations and medical treatments made her condition worse and left her discouraged and embittered. In 1929, when she was thirty-four years old, a friend who had read *Man's Supreme Inheritance* persuaded her to go to London and "take a gamble" on the Alexander Technique. With great scepticism she began a two-month series of daily lessons. The unexpected changes she observed in herself during the course of the lessons (the redevelopment of wasted muscles in her legs, a new use of her arms, a sense of tranquillity she had never experienced since she first had infantile paralysis) carried so much conviction that she determined to take the training course for teachers when the opportunity presented itself two years later. The narrative of her experiences in London that culminated in her learning to dance and ride horseback is a touching account of special interest because she was, as she put it, "a badly handicapped person," and the changes she observed in herself were not typical of the changes reported by other pupils. Some changes were gradual and took place almost unnoticed, as when she discovered one morning that her right heel, which had been drawn up for twenty years, was touching the floor on a level with the left. Other changes, however, were accompanied by pain and discomfort. She explains the latter as part of a righting process that "appears to right the body in a steady, cumulative way. . . . At intervals this righting process mounts up, and then a basic change takes place. At such times I might have an uncomfortable manifestation as well as severe fatigue but always after such a change I would be markedly improved in one form or another and have a considerable increase in strength and energy" (p. 91).

Lulie Westfeldt's narrative is also of value for the picture it gives of Alexander's teaching at what was apparently a transitional period in his development of the Technique. He was becoming increasingly skilled in the use of his hands and less dependent on words to convey his meaning. (He told me later that by this time he was able to get in three days results that had taken him three weeks before.) When the pupil perceives directly through the kinaesthetic sense and can compare a habitual with a non-habitual way of doing something, he doesn't need words in order to grasp the significance of the experience. Alexander put it succinctly in a remark reported by Lulie Westfeldt (p. 71): "If we become sensorily aware of doing a harmful thing to ourselves, we can cease doing it." The key word here is "sensorily."

After the death of his wife in 1933 A. R. Alexander moved to Boston and established his own practice in the United States. From that time on the training of teachers rested entirely with F. M., except for three years during the war when A. R. again took over the training course.

7

The Universal Constant in Living

One has to make the discovery for oneself, starting from scratch, and to find what old F. M. Alexander called "the means whereby," without which good intentions merely pave hell and the idealist remains an ineffectual, self-destructive and other-destructive "end-gainer."

Aldous Huxley

"THE UPPER CLASSES," A. R. Alexander once said, "are never any help to you. When one of them discovers the Technique, he never tells anybody else about it. He likes to keep it for himself." It was different with literary people. They liked to share the knowledge of something they had discovered, even if they didn't make much use of it for themselves. Bernard Shaw was eighty when he had a "full course" of forty lessons from F. M. He undoubtedly benefited from them (he lived to be ninety-four), but the principal use to which he put the knowledge was for ammunition to attack Pavlov, with whose ideas and practice he carried on a running battle. Alexander, Shaw wrote, "having the true scientific spirit and industry," set out to discover what he was doing to disable himself while he was speaking. "In the end he found this out and a great deal more as well. He established not only the beginnings of a far-reaching science of the apparently involuntary movements we call reflexes, but a technique of correction and self-control which forms a substantial addition to our very slender resources in personal education." Pavlov, Shaw went on to say, investigated the same subject, but he did it "by practising the horrible voodoo into which professional medical research had lapsed in the nineteenth century." Pavlov was "not by nature a bad man" but "well-meaning, intelligent and devoted to science." But because he was corrupted by the prevailing academic atmosphere he was "forced to mutilate and torment dogs instead of discovering the methods by which humane unofficial investigators were meanwhile finding out all that he was looking for." If he had not been morally blinded by his barbarous method of research, he "might have shared the laurels of Alexander."

Of all the literary people who passed through the hands of F. M. Alexander, Aldous Huxley (1894–1963) did the most to bring the Technique to the attention of the reading public. For Huxley himself, it was a means for breaking out of "the chains of determinism" and opening the way to physical and spiritual experiences that were not possible for him before.

Aldous Huxley in the 1920s had represented the ultimate in freedom from all the "conventional orthodoxies, officious humbug, and sexual taboos" that society had inherited from the Victorians. In those days he believed with Pavlov and Watson that all behaviour is determined by either genetic or environmental factors. He rejected Christian morality and the doctrine of freewill as bankrupt. ("What a lot of satisfaction I got out of old Pavlov when I first read him. . . . No nonsense about free-will, goodness, truth and all the rest.") He found no comfort in science, however, which took away the bases of conventional morality but seemed to Huxley to leave man with nothing but boredom to put in their place. Scientists in his novels are as incompetent in their human relations as clergymen. Shearwater in *Antic Hay* and Lord Edward Tantamount in *Point Counter Point*, both of them eminent physiologists and authorities on sexual responses in animals, are represented as socially and sexually inept. The *reductio ad absurdum* of science was, of course, *Brave New World* (1930), but Huxley had used the theme as early as 1921 in *Crome Yellow* with Scogan's vision of "vast state incubators with their rows and rows of gravid bottles to supply the world with a scientifically selected population."

Romantic love, when it is treated at all in the early novels, is either a subject for mockery or a source of sorrow. But the sensuous men and sensuous women whom Huxley sets as foils or traps for the romantics do not fare any better. Old age and disease creep upon them, take away their physical charm, and leave them defenceless and absurd. In his pages, virtue is ridiculous but so is vice, and the wicked do not flourish.

In spite of Huxley's cynicism about the human condition he was not reconciled to the view that life is meaningless. Mass solutions, however, did not appeal to him. He found both communism and fascism repulsive. He was never caught up in the emotions of a crowd and believed that change, if it came at all, had to come through the individual. At one time he seemed prepared to follow D. H. Lawrence into a new humanism that established a harmony of the person, with instinct rather than intellect striking the dominant chord. Huxley, however, was too much of an intellectual to "think with his blood" as Lawrence advocated. Lawrence's method for passing beyond the individual, Huxley once said, "led not toward light and freedom, but into a visceral, subhuman night like that of Jonah in his whale."

Instead of Lawrence's solution Huxley would have preferred that of the mystics. His brother Julian said: "One of Aldous' major preoccupations was how to achieve self-transcendence while yet remaining a committed social being—how to escape from the prison bars of self and the pressure of here and now into realms of pure goodness and pure enjoyment." Aldous had always felt an interest in Oriental thought. He referred to Buddhism in his letters as early as 1918 and by the middle of the 1920s he was talking familiarly of Lao-tzu and the practice of yoga as possible means for solving what he called "the most vital problem—the ethical and emotional" (*Letters*, p. 245). His attempts to practice yoga exercises, however, were not successful at this time—they were too arduous and demanding and struck him as a little ridiculous. In "The Claxtons" (1930) he gives a satirical account of such attempts, referring to yoga as "the mystical substitute for Cascara."

In 1929 or 1930 after a meeting with Gerald Heard (author of *The Third Morality* and *Pain, Sex and Time*), who was advocating a "non-theological practice of meditation," Huxley's hope for a transcendental solution to his problems was revived. "From this time on," says Ronald Clark, one of his biographers, "Huxley's largely negative attitude gradually changed into a mounting belief that all problems might be solved by a spiritual intuition which rose triumphantly from that borderland between mind and matter that had intrigued his grandfather." The means for making the transition escaped him, however. He now knew what he wanted to do and what he ought to do, but like the self-bound heroes of his own novels he was unable to change. In Huxley the split between the mind and the body, which Lawrence deplored, was especially marked. Six feet four, gangling, stooped, nearsighted and awkward, he reminded himself of "the young man from Thermopylae who never did anything properly." He was subject to fatigue and insomnia and had a very weak stomach. As an extreme ectomorph (Huxley was delighted with W. E. Sheldon's concept of the somatotype as a predictor of behaviour) he had very little postural tonus to hold him up. A friend, Naomi Mitchison, described him in 1915 as "long and dreadfully vulnerable looking. . . . He draped himself over things, his long legs dangling across the backs of chairs and sofas." Though thoughts came easily to him when he was at a typewriter or talking in a small group, he was physically afraid to speak in public. T. S. Eliot described a literary dinner where both he and Huxley were scheduled to speak. Huxley stood up first after lighting a large cigar. Whether from the tobacco or the stress of speaking he suddenly jack-knifed forward and had to be carried out by three of the male guests. After 1930 he wanted very much to lecture on behalf of the peace movement that Gerald Heard was sponsoring, but he was afraid to accept a speaking engagement.

Huxley's malaise culminated when he was writing *Eyeless in Gaza*. He began it in November 1932, but two years later it was still unfinished and he was suffering acutely from depression and insomnia. The novel may have been the precipitating factor. Technically, it was his most ambitious work to date, covering a time span of thirty years and making use of a difficult cinematic device of juxtaposing in sequence the separate segments from four different periods in the hero's life. Like all of his novels, it is a *roman à clef*, but more than the others it incorporates his most painful memories—his mother's death from cancer, her funeral, his father's remarriage, and his brother's suicide. It also incorporates a more searching analysis of his own character—portraying his hero at forty-two as a rationalizing hedonist incapable of true love or passion. His wife said that she hated the novel "because of the misery it has caused us," and it is easy to imagine how it had done so. It was still unfinished in 1935, and by this time Huxley was so exhausted that he could compose only while lying on his back with the typewriter on his chest.

I do not know who it was who introduced Huxley to Alexander. It could have been one of a number of his friends. "Going to Alexander" was a fashionable thing to do in the circles in which the Huxleys moved. Sometime in the fall of 1935, at any rate, Huxley began having daily lessons in the Technique. His general condition soon improved, and by the end of the year he was speaking in public. In February 1936 his wife wrote: "Alexander has certainly made a new and unrecognisable person of Aldous, not physically only but mentally and therefore morally. Or rather, he has brought out, actively, all we, Aldous's best friends, know never came out either in the novels or with strangers." Huxley went back to the book and solved the problem of how to end it by introducing Alexander in the person of Miller, the medical anthropologist, as the redemptive figure who showed the hero how to change. *Eyeless in Gaza* was published in July 1936. Into the person of Miller, Huxley also incorporated, ironically, a part of Gerald Heard, whom Alexander detested, and a part of Dr. McDonagh, a fashionable but unorthodox physician to whom Alexander often referred his pupils. The scattered references to the Alexander Technique that it contains were given a more formal expression in *Ends and Means*, which appeared the following year. Further references to the Technique can be found in Huxley's writings from then on. He made it the basis of his "Education of an Amphibian" in *Tomorrow and Tomorrow and Tomorrow*, in 1954 he wrote an introduction to Louise Morgan's popular treatise on Alexander and his work, *Inside Yourself*. While he was writing *Island* in 1960 he studied the Technique with me; and he talked about it that fall in his Massachusetts Institute of Technology (MIT) lectures, "What a Piece of Work is a Man." Three letters I received from him the year before he died show that his interest had not lapsed.

Huxley's attitude toward the Alexander Technique fluctuated over the years. At times he seemed to think of it as a basic principle essential to educational change. At others he lumped it into an educational package along with whatever mind-expanding technique interested him at the time—Zen, yoga, Bonpensière, the Bates Method, autohypnosis or Jacobsonian relaxation. Alexander sometimes had doubts whether Aldous really understood the Technique, but he was grateful for the publicity his writings brought. A whole succession of new pupils (myself included), who would probably never have heard of the Alexander Technique if it had not been for Huxley's endorsement in *Ends and Means*, began having lessons either with F. M. in London or with A. R. in Boston or New York.

F. M. celebrated his seventieth birthday a few months before World War II broke out. As had happened during the first world war, the teaching practice was drastically reduced. Pupils from abroad went home; students in the training course were drawn into the armed services; and private pupils were finding it difficult to get into London for lessons. For safety's sake the little school was moved from Bexhill in Kent to a remote house in Wiltshire away from the route of the bombers. The problems of teaching the Technique in wartime were intensified after Dunkirk. Because of his anti-German pronouncements, F. M.'s name was said to be on Hitler's "enemies list"; and in any event there seemed to be no future for the work in England if the projected invasion took place. On July 8, 1940, the S. S. *Monarch of Bermuda* was scheduled to sail from Scotland with a contingent of six hundred children who were being sent to live with families in Canada and the United States. With the help of all concerned Alexander contrived to be on it. In his party were eight children from the school and six adults, among them Ethel Webb, who had again been invited to visit her friends at Columbia, and two other teachers, Margaret Goldie and Irene Stewart. The *Monarch of Bermuda* was part of an armed convoy which, unknown to passengers and crew, carried two and half billion dollars' worth of gold coins, bullion and securities from the Bank of England for safekeeping in Canada. Sailing at high speed and without lights the ship followed a zigzag course across the Atlantic, putting into Halifax harbour with its cargo of children and gold on July 13. After a brief stay in Canada, F. M. and the others in the party who had American visas came on to the United States. The rest remained in Toronto until suitable arrangements could be made for the school.

Among the few possessions that F. M. managed to take with him in the hurried departure from England was the manuscript of a new book, *The Universal Constant in Living*, which was published by Dutton the following year, 1941. The book has very little organization and can only be considered as a long, disconnected appendix to the earlier books. For one who is familiar with the Technique, however, *The Universal Constant* contains much that is of interest. It starts out with the arresting sentence: "Few of us hitherto have given consideration to the question of the extent to which we are individually responsible for the ills that our flesh is heir to." It is not so much what we have done in the past or what has been done to us that causes our troubles but what we are doing to ourselves through "the faulty and often harmful manner in which we use ourselves in our daily activities and even during sleep." Alexander had advanced the concept of "use" in his previous book, but many of his readers failed to grasp what he was trying to say. Though everything he said was based on the principle of "the indissoluble *unity* of the human organism," they insisted on treating it as if it applied to *separate* parts. Whether you are using your hands in some factory job or your reasoning processes in "education, religion, politics or science," the rôle of the organism is the same. Your hands can be highly skilled and your reasoning can be brilliant, but if you are using the organism itself badly by interfering with the primary control, this wrong use will be "a constant influence for ill." Conversely, "an improving manner of use" will exert a constant influence for good "in the restoration and maintenance of psycho-physical efficiency."

Once you have divided the organism into parts—body and mind, or body, mind and soul—it is easy to find something besides yourself to blame for your troubles. Shifting of responsibility from the whole to the part is deeply rooted in Western thought. "It was not I, it was my tongue that swore"; "if thy right hand offend thee, cut it off." It did not occur to Coleridge, the drug-addicted poet-philosopher, to blame himself for the woes that came upon him in old age, "this drooping gait, this altered size." It was his body's fault—"this body that does me grievous wrong." When he was young, it was very different: "nought cared this body for wind or weather when youth and I lived in't together."

Examples could be multiplied indefinitely. Because this form of the pathetic fallacy is so common, it is often difficult to recognize it—like the "hidden figure" in a perceptual illusion. Once it has been recognized, however, it will be seen again and again. When you understand the concept of "use," you will stop saying you have a "bad back" or a "tennis elbow" or an "Oedipus complex" or a "phobia for cats" and find out what you are doing that keeps you from getting over it. When Alexander realized that "his doing was his undoing," he was on the road to recovery.

The rest of the book is devoted almost entirely to illustrating the influence of use upon functioning. A long chapter on "Use in Relation to Diagnosis and Disease" has a brief recapitulation of the personal narrative in *The Use of the Self* (as a key to the discussion of several medical histories of patients referred to him by doctors. The histories are prefaced by a letter that had been published in the *British Medical Journal* (May 29, 1937) and signed by nineteen physicians calling for an investigation of the Technique which would lead to including it in the medical curriculum. Two of the most interesting cases, osteoarthritis and tic douloureux, are discussed in considerable detail and include the observations over a period of time by the attending physician and the patient as well as the analysis by Alexander. The chapter concludes with an account of how the Technique was applied in a case of difficult childbirth. Alexander quoted from Anthony Ludovici, who said in *The Truth about Childbirth* (1937) that in the "faulty use of self" with the "vicious bodily coordination" that accompanies it "we have a sufficient amount of mischief to impair not only the course of pregnancy but also and above all that of childbirth." Ludovici referred at this point to Alexander, who, long before the talk of "natural childbirth" and "childbirth without fear," had been teaching women how not to interfere with the normal process of gestation and delivery.

The Universal Constant in Living is more like a scrapbook than an ordinary book. Besides the case histories and letters from doctors and patients, it incorporates news stories, reports of speeches, articles from medical journals and popular magazines, newspaper photographs, quotations from previous books by Alexander, and an unpublished essay by Aldous Huxley on army training, all woven together with a running commentary by Alexander. In this mosaic three pieces that deserve special comment are the excerpts from two articles by medical doctors who attempt to explain the Technique in terms of muscular mechanisms; and an "appreciation" by the American biologist George E. Coghill.

Dr. Andrew Murdoch, at a meeting of the Sussex Branch of the British Medical Association (of which he was president), read a paper on "The Function of the Sub-occipital Muscles: The Key to Posture, Use and Functioning." Murdoch's theory is that the seven pairs of small muscles that connect the first two vertebrae with the occiput are "the primary movers of the Cranial Globe" (which Murdoch describes as "a weighty mass poised on the summit of the vertebral column") and "the primary mechanism used in the control of ourselves." In other words, the suboccipital muscle group is Alexander's primary control. Murdoch's theory appealed to many people who were delighted to think that a real "primary control" had actually been discovered. I do not subscribe to this view, however. Though these muscles are undoubtedly of great importance in maintaining the balance of the head against gravity, they could scarcely be described as its "primary movers." (The head is not poised on the top of the vertebral column like a pumpkin on a pole; it is in unstable equilibrium and would fall forward if the muscles and ligaments attached to it were cut.) The "primary movers" must be the surface muscles, which are longer, have better leverage, and can contract more quickly. In any event it is bootless to equate the primary control with any one anatomical entity which can be displayed by dissecting a cadaver, or to attempt, as Murdoch suggests, to teach the Alexander Technique by training pupils in the conscious use of specific muscles.

More persuasive is the paper by Dr. Mungo Douglas, "Reorientation of the View Point upon the Study of Anatomy." Douglas also explained Alexander's discovery and technique in terms of muscular anatomy. The function of muscle, he said, is twofold: to "perform movements of parts about joints, and maintain relations of parts to parts." Of the two, the second is the more important. In muscular terms what Alexander discovered was that "there were certain functions certain groups of muscles could not be considered to perform, although human beings so used them," and that by the use of inhibition these wrong usages of muscle could be stopped, "whereupon the remaining usages of these groups could be used both to produce movements of parts about joints, and maintain relations of parts to parts with least friction." Douglas did not consider that the function of the suboccipital system of muscles was to move the cranial globe but to establish "the primary relation upon which all more ultimate relations depend." Neither Murdoch nor

Douglas produced any experimental or clinical data to support their views. Their papers are valuable as examples of how anatomical knowledge can be used to test Alexander's theories about the use of the organism.

The most important document incorporated into *The Universal Constant* is Coghill's "Appreciation." George E. Coghill (1872-1941), after a distinguished career in biology and comparative anatomy (Sir Julian Huxley placed him "among the twenty outstanding biological scientists of our time"), had retired to a small farm in Gainesville, Florida, where he continued to do research on animal locomotion.

When he was a student at Brown University, Coghill was strongly influenced by the experimental psychologist Professor E. B. Delabarre, who had been trained by William James. Torn between psychology and biology, Coghill chose a line of research in which he was able to combine the two interests. The ninety-nine research papers cited by Herrick in his biography (*George Ellett Coghill*, 1949) cover a wide variety of topics but all have bearing on the central aim of the research that was to correlate the development of behaviour with the development of anatomical structure. "If there should prove to be order in the development of behaviour," he wrote, "common principles of growth should maintain in the two fields: in the development of behaviour and in the development of the nervous system" (Herrick, p. 79). The animal he chose for his study was amblystoma, a species of salamander which recommended itself because of its simple behaviour and its correspondingly simple nervous system. In a series of detailed and painstaking observations made over a period of more than thirty years he followed the development of motility and structural change from the earliest manifestations in the embryo. From these studies he derived principles of behaviour that proved productive in psychology as well as in biology. Movement, Coghill said, was integrated from the start, with the "total pattern" of the head and trunk dominating the "partial patterns" of the limbs. The primary function of the nervous system, he said, was to maintain the integrity of the individual "while the behaviour pattern expands" (Herrick, p. 122). In the total pattern of behaviour there were two parts, "one overt or excitatory and the other covert or inhibitory." The inhibitory factor was essential for the successful execution of specific reflexes (Herrick, pp. 110, 107).

Because of the primacy of the total pattern, Coghill maintained that there were no grounds for adopting a deterministic or fatalistic position. Though spontaneity gradually decreases with the establishment of conditioned reflexes (which like unconditioned reflexes "emerge on the motor side from a field of general activity"), the capacity for spontaneous and creative action is never lost. "Man," Coghill said, "is a mechanism which, within his limitations of life, sensitivity and growth, is creating and operating himself."

Coghill established an international reputation with the publication in 1929 of his three London lectures, *Anatomy and the Problem of Behaviour.* The book was hailed as a classic and had a strong influence in scientific circles throughout Europe. In the course of his stay in England Coghill met and conversed with leaders in European science. Professor H. A. Harris, who had sponsored the London lectures, wrote to Herrick that Coghill's book was "one of the first attempts to give an anatomical basis to behaviourism" (Herrick, p. 6).

Arthur F. Busch, who wrote a regular column for the *Brooklyn Citizen* under the pen name of Michael March, brought the work of Alexander to the attention of Coghill. Busch was a pupil of A. R. Alexander's and wrote frequently about the Technique in his column. Apropos of Alexander's discovery Coghill wrote: "It is a very different thing to state a theory and to demonstrate it as a fact. It is the demonstration that places the concept on a scientific foundation." Alexander had an opportunity to demonstrate his principle to Coghill a few months before Coghill's death in July 1941. He spent a weekend in Gainesville and gave Coghill several lessons in the Technique. In his "Appreciation" Coghill described the demonstration: "He enabled me to prevent misdirection of the muscles of my neck and back and to bring about a use of these muscles that determined the relative position of my head and neck to my body and so on to my limbs, bringing my thighs into the abducted position. This led to changes throughout my body and limbs associated with a pattern of behaviour more natural (in agreement with the total pattern) for the act of getting on my feet. The whole procedure was calculated to occupy my brain with the projection of directive messages that would enable me to acquire conscious control of the proprioceptive component of the reflex mechanism involved. The projection of the directed messages, Mr. Alexander considers, stimulated nervous and motor activity that was associated with better conditions. This leads to the belief that the motor paths of the spinal cord and the nerve paths through the brain associated with the total pattern were again being used."

The demonstration was the more striking since Coghill at the time was severely crippled with arthritis and had a serious heart condition. In his discussion of the experience Coghill relates Alexander's work to his own and concludes with the statement: "I regard his methods as thoroughly scientific and educationally sound."

As a footnote to this account Alexander told me that while he was in Gainesville he had an opportunity to demonstrate the principle of the primary control with one of Coghill's chickens as well as with Coghill himself. The chicken, which was one of a group of newly hatched chicks, was walking around in a peculiar fashion which intrigued and perplexed Coghill. Alexander picked it up, examined it carefully, and discovered that a bit of yolk-covered shell was caught in the down at the back of the chicken's neck and was pulling the head back and down. Alexander freed the neck from the shell and the chicken ran off, its gait indistinguishable from that of the others.

Coghill's death intervened before another meeting could be arranged between the two men. Their brief association meant a great deal to Alexander. It was the first time he had received the endorsement of a scientist of Coghill's eminence. Though this endorsement did not lead to a general acceptance of Alexander's idea, it confirmed him in his belief that he had discovered a universal principle of behaviour.

8

The Two Brothers

The ideal condition would be, I admit,
That man should be right by instinct;
But since we are all too likely to go astray,
The reasonable thing is to learn from those who can teach.

Sophocles, *Antigone*

I HAD MY FIRST lesson from F. M. Alexander in September 1940. He was staying at a seaside hotel in Southwest Harbor, Maine, giving lessons to a few of his old pupils who summered on Mount Desert Island, and putting finishing touches on *The Universal Constant in Living*. My lesson was scheduled for the middle of the morning at a cottage belonging to Mrs. Wendell T. Bush, whose husband was the professor of philosophy at Columbia who was said to have introduced Alexander to Dewey.

As I waited, trying to imagine what he would look like, I suddenly realized that he was standing in the doorway looking at me and that I had not heard him approach. He was shorter than I expected, but he had an easy, upright carriage and gave the impression of being at his full height without making any effort to be there. His face was alert, with a bright, quizzical look in the eyes and a slightly ironic twist to the mouth. (Huxley said that Dr. Miller, who was modelled after Alexander, had "a mouth like an inquisitor's. But the inquisitor had forgotten himself and learned to smile.") His hair was white but he did not wear glasses, and in voice, manner and movement he seemed much younger than I knew him to be. He gave this impression of youthfulness to everyone. A child who was introduced to him that summer and was puzzled at his being called F. M. referred to him afterwards as "the young man with the funny name."

Nothing spectacular happened in the lesson (as it had in my first lesson with A. R.), but my awareness must have been heightened. That night I was wakened by a thunderstorm and got up to close my window. Forgetting that I was in a country hotel and that the window was not balanced by a counterweight, I loosened the catch, letting the window crash down onto my finger. I had never known how to cope with this kind of pain, but had always been engulfed by the throbbing agony of the sensation. This time, undoubtedly as a consequence of the lesson that morning, I perceived the sensation as a pattern with time–space values and found that I could inhibit the surges of tension that were passing in waves from my neck down my shoulder and arm to my finger. As I sustained the inhibition by keeping the awareness of my head and neck central and my finger peripheral, the sensation changed from ischaemic pain to a glowing warmth as blood began to flow back into my finger. In the morning there was nothing to remind me of the episode except a thin red line across the nail.

Pain is a topic that has been extensively studied, but its mysteries have not been solved. Experimental pain does not provide meaningful answers because it can be terminated at will by the subject. Clinical pain is real enough, but it is hard to study experimentally. I believe that the mystery can be solved only by using clinical subjects who have previously been taught to observe their sensations as stimulus–response patterns and can establish an inhibitory control over the response. For me the experience was an example of one-trial learning. The practical insight which it gave me into the mechanism and management of pain has proved invaluable since.

I had one more lesson before driving back to Providence to resume my teaching at Brown University. As soon as I could do so I arranged to have further lessons with the Alexanders. A. R. was already in Boston. He was joined in October by F. M., and the two brothers divided their time with alternate weeks in New York. Sometimes their stays in Boston overlapped, and once I remember that both of them worked with me together. It was an impressive experience, but I am not sure now that I learned anything from it. This multiple "laying on of hands" (F. M. would sometimes bring in two assistants and together they would move the pupil around like a Japanese puppet) seems to me now of dubious value as a teaching device.

The pupil is given more kinaesthetic information that he can integrate or absorb, and gains nothing that he can build on or put to practical use. At the time, however, I had no basis for making a critical judgement and accepted whatever the Alexanders did as the only way to do it.

Besides a single-hearted devotion to their work, the Alexander brothers shared a taste for good food well prepared and an enthusiasm for horse racing. In eating they were connoisseurs rather than gourmets, preferring English to French cooking. What they demanded in food was quality. They had been brought up on a farm in Tasmania where the food was grown on virgin soil and even the farm animals were fed only the best. "Buy only the best food," their father told them when they left home for the city, "even if you can only afford a little of it." Americans, they observed, did just the opposite; quantity was what they prized and they would eat anything so long as it was sweet enough and could be consumed in a hurry. F. M. believed that the sense of taste was just as important as other senses, but that, like kinaesthesia, it was no longer reliable ("debauched" was F. M.'s word for describing the unreliability of the senses). If the sense of taste were reliable, he said, Americans would refuse to eat most of the food that was sold in the markets or served in the restaurants. Anyone with a sense of taste would know, for example that the ham and bacon sold over here came from hogs that had been wrongly fed. He and his brother believed in organic gardening because a vegetable grown that way tasted better and obviously was better for you. They were not vegetarians, however, and thought that Bernard Shaw would have been better off if he had eaten a good steak occasionally.

Everyone who was acquainted with the Alexanders was aware of their knowledge of horses, which, like their knowledge of food, they had acquired at an early age. In London both brothers went riding for recreation (in *Who's Who* F. M. listed his recreations as "riding, shooting, theatre"), and they always attended race meetings when they could spare the time from teaching. Both of them were devoted to betting. In Boston A. R. tried never to schedule lessons when the horses were running at Suffolk Downs or Narragansett. He told me that if he had wanted to devote all of his time to it he would have made a great deal more money on horse racing than on teaching.

One day (it was the Fourth of July, as I remember) I was invited to drive F. M. and A. R. to Suffolk Downs (neither of the brothers drove a car). This was my first visit to a racetrack and I knew nothing about horses. However, I watched the two of them carefully as they consulted their racing cards and dope sheets or walked over to inspect the horses as they were led past the rail. Before the last race I decided to imitate them as best I could and place a small bet myself. To my surprise, my horse came in first, and, as I found out later, I was the only one who had picked a winner. I took the two brothers out to dinner with my winnings, but they never invited me again.

In appearance and manner the two were very different. F. M., the older in years, was younger in behaviour. He was more of an extrovert than his brother and more articulate. He was an excellent mimic and liked to illustrate the points he was making by acting out particular examples of "bad use" which he had observed in the course of his teaching. He would also enliven his lessons with anecdotes about his life in Australia and occasionally with declamations—the opening chapter from *The Tale of Two Cities* or Hood's "Dream of Eugene Aram"—which he retained from his days as a reciter. Two of his favourites, "The Man from Snowy River" and "The Billiard Marker's Story" ("It was the billiard marker at the Gin and Cloves Hotel . . . ."), came from a collection of Australian ballads by A. B. Patterson (*The Man from Snowy River and Other Verses*, London: Macmillan, 1927). And there was always Shakespeare. "He would quote you Shakespeare at the drop of a hat," Margaret Goldie said. F. M. thought that Shakespeare more than anyone saw what was happening to modern man. I can remember the eloquence with which he quoted Hamlet's bitter indictment starting with "What a piece of work is a man" and ending with "Man delights not me!"

In teaching he had a way, which I found disconcerting, of stepping back from time to time to look critically at his pupil as if he were painting a portrait. James Harvey Robinson said: "He actually remodels the body as a sculptor models the clay." I once saw him working with a sixteen-year-old girl who was severely afflicted with scoliosis. Deftly and skilfully, making only the slightest of changes at one time, he gradually brought her up until she appeared to be two or three inches taller and almost symmetrical. As long as he kept his hands at her back and head, she was able to walk around without any loss of symmetry. When he removed his hands, her body slowly settled back, or almost back, to where it had been before.

When I knew F. M., he had very little to say about "directive orders" or "thinking." I assumed that he was satisfied that I knew how to "order" and that I was giving him the cooperation he needed. He seemed to be getting the effects he wanted, at any rate. In this regard, A. R. was quite different. He was always stopping a pupil and telling him he was "feeling, not thinking," by which he meant that the pupil had become either stiff or heavy and was not responding to the direction of his hands. It was very easy in a lesson to let your mind wander and be unaware of what was going on, but A. R. never let you get away with this for very long. He had none of his brother's showmanship and was, perhaps, less skilful with his hands. He was very patient and seemed determined to get his points across. (I sometimes had the feeling that F. M. lost interest in a pupil after he had made dramatic changes and was bored with teaching him anything further.) A. R., since he was not the discoverer but had to be taught the Technique himself, had more understanding of the problems involved in learning. Neither of the brothers suffered fools gladly, however. Like so many people who know but one language, they believed in a one-to-one relation between the word and the thing. (F. M. had no use for Korzybski or general semantics). They were confident that the words they used to describe what they did were the best that could be found. If a pupil did not understand, they repeated the explanation verbatim, assuring him that ultimately it would be perfectly clear. One day when I was having trouble understanding the relation between my thinking and the kinaesthetic experiences A. R. was giving me, he said, "Be patient; stick to principle; and it will all open up like a great cauliflower." I did not understand what this meant but it was somehow reassuring.

It was more reassuring coming from A. R. than it would have from F. M. A. R. had had greater handicaps to overcome than F. M.'s loss of voice. Typhoid fever had left him with badly impaired vision, and shortly after the war he suffered a severe back injury. He had been riding in Hyde Park one morning when he spotted his wife standing on the sidewalk with their young son. As A. R. sat there talking with them, he took his feet out of the stirrups for a moment just as a motor car roared by. The horse reared up and threw him to the ground, shattering the base of his spine. The doctors told him he could never walk again, and for eighteen months he lay in a darkened room with nothing to do (he could not read) but practice inhibition and directive orders. In the end he was able to prove the doctors wrong by walking, first with two canes and then with one. When I knew him, he used the cane only to steady himself, never coming down on it heavily, and could walk, with a curious swaying motion, for a considerable distance, his trunk very upright and his legs swinging smoothly from the hips. His handicap did not keep him from going to the races or walking out to his favourite restaurant or sitting on a bench in the parkway of Commonwealth Avenue smoking his pipe and observing the passers-by with an appraising air. One of them stopped in front of him one day and said, "Sir, I've watched you for a long time and I wish I knew what you have that other people don't have." "I'll warrant you do," said A. R. laconically, and swinging up onto his cane he returned to the Braemore Hotel without another word. He made no attempt to sell the Technique. In fact, he always treated prospective pupils with suspicion until he was convinced that they had a legitimate interest in learning. He would not accept therapists of any kind or teachers of physical education, who, he was sure, wanted merely to pick up a few new ideas to enliven their own teaching and be able to say that they were using the Alexander Technique. He was inclined to extend this suspicion to doctors, who, because of their training, were seldom able, he believed, to accept the idea of mind-body unity. They wanted to "turn it into a doing" and then say that there was nothing in it. On one occasion A. R. was so exasperated at this medical obtuseness that he said to me, "If another doctor wants lessons from me he will have to ask for them on his hands and knees!"

F. M. liked to relieve the monotony of a lesson by putting the pupil into a "position of mechanical advantage," which was usually a position he would never get into by himself and could maintain only by the continuous "giving of orders" so as not to become either heavy or stiff. A favourite was the "monkey position," or "monkey" for short. The pupil stood with his feet quite apart and the toes pointing out. While he directed his neck to relax, F. M. manipulated his head in such a way that the knees and hips flexed simultaneously while the back lengthened and rotated forward, allowing the arms to swing.

The procedure produced a state of plastic tonus throughout the extensor system. As long as the neck remained free and the head was directed "forward and up," the position could be maintained or changed without muscular effort, since the parts were in dynamic balance. The monkey position is useful when bending over a sink or a table, since it does not tire the back or legs. It looks distinctly odd to the uninitiated, however, and used to mystify strangers if they visited the training course and found three or four pupils "in monkey."

Courtesy of the author

Fig. 1. A. R. Alexander (1874–1947)

A. R. made little use of special positions except for demonstration purposes. Because he was unsteady on his legs, he moved around very little but sat on a low sofa at right angles to the pupil, who was seated on a chair beside him. He was skilful with his hands, which for most of the time he was using above shoulder level. As long as the pupil was thinking or "ordering," A. R. could move him easily in and out of the chair with a hand at his arm or back. The instant he stopped thinking, however, it would be detected at once. "That's not Alexander," he would sometimes say; "that's just Jacobson" (if you were heavy) or, "that's Mensendieck" (if you were stiff).

During my early lessons with A. R., getting in and out of a chair was a regular ritual. I always knew that at some point during a lesson I would be asked to get up and that if I inhibited my response to this stimulus and "thought my way out of the chair," it would be a remarkably easy and pleasant experience; but that if I "tried to be right," I was in for a long argument which could be ended only by admitting I was wrong and did not know how to think. The procedure was a kind of laboratory exercise in the cause and control of anxiety. I could feel myself becoming anxious during the course of the lesson. I remembered what a pleasant and desirable experience it was to move up against gravity without effort; I remembered that I could not have the experience unless I could inhibit my habitual response to the stimulus to get up; I remembered that if I did not inhibit I would be a dead weight in Alexander's hands and that he might not be able to support me. All of these memories united to produce a marked state of anxiety, which was further heightened when I remembered that I had driven all the way from Providence and was paying dearly for a half-hour lesson. It was this final consideration that turned the tide. I decided that if I was going to justify my expenditure of time and money I must try to inhibit as best I could even if I did not understand how it worked. The best place to begin, I thought, might be to stop being "anxious about being anxious" and to find out what I was actually doing. In this way I would at least learn something about myself even if I did not get out of the chair. This was an intelligent rather than an emotional response to the situation. The level of my anxiety was reduced as soon as I was able to look at it objectively. This change from my habitual behaviour was immediately reinforced by the freedom and ease with which I found myself moving. I do not now believe that it is necessary to heighten a pupil's anxiety during a lesson in order to teach him how to control it. This was A. R.'s way, however.

A. R. had his own concept of the directive orders. He did not introduce them until after I had had several lessons; had clearly perceived the kinaesthetic effect of lightness; and had associated it with the absence of my habitual pattern of tension. His view, as I understood it, was that orders (directing your neck to relax, your head to go forward and up, to lengthen and widen your back), whether verbalized or not, were an aid to thinking but not a substitute for it; that you could "give orders" without thinking; and that there were occasions (for example, talking) when you had to be able to think without giving orders. He voiced these objections to me at one time, and I had the feeling that he would have given up the concept altogether if it had not been stated so explicitly in the books.

Having lessons from each of the Alexander brothers gave me a perspective that I do not believe I would have obtained if I had worked with only one of them. It was much easier to see that there was a fundamental principle involved that had nothing to do with the personality of the teacher or his particular way of teaching.

During October and November 1940 an intensive search was made to find suitable living quarters for the children and teachers whom F. M. had left behind in Toronto. The problem was solved early in December when the American Unitarian Association offered the use of the Whitney Homestead, a rest home in Stow, Massachusetts, twenty miles west of Boston. It took a while to get the Homestead into working order, and the first contingent of children did not arrive in Boston until January 28, 1941. They were met at the Back Bay Station by A. R. and a reporter from the *Boston Post*, which featured the story on the front page under the headline: WHEN DO WE EAT? REFUGEES' QUERY. A. R. had handed the reporter a statement from F. M. describing the aims of the school. These were printed as "self-explanatory" at the end of the article, with the rest of the space devoted to the human-interest aspects of the story—the bombing, the submarines that the ship outran, and the battleship and cruiser escort. The names of the children were given and the fact duly noted that two were grandchildren of Lord Camrose and one a relative of Lord Halifax. The reporter was clearly mystified by A. R., whom he described as "a widely respected religionist." This was ironic, since it was A. R.'s opinion that religion interfered with learning the Technique.

During the winter of 1940–41 I came to Boston or Stow as often as I could to have lessons with one of the Alexanders. I was beginning to realize that the potential benefit of the Technique for my health and happiness was much greater than I had supposed at the start. I had also begun to realize the vast implications of the Technique (or of the principles it embodied) for education and the health sciences; and to feel more and more frustrated by the thought that these implications might never be recognized. Both of the Alexanders were in their seventies; very few teachers had been trained; and now because of the war the training had stopped. There seemed to be a very real possibility that the Alexander Technique would become a lost art, surviving only as an obscure reference (which no one would understand) in annotated editions of Dewey, Huxley or Shaw. These considerations all weighed strongly with me, and when F. M. offered to train me as a teacher I decided that I ought to take advantage of the opportunity, though I was cautious and conservative by nature and lacked the pioneer spirit. My principal reason for hesitating was the fear that I would not be successful as a teacher because I had no manual dexterity. When I brought this question up to A. R., however, he reassured me ("Never fear!" was the expression he used) that this was not a handicap and might even prove an asset, since I would be starting from scratch without any wrong ideas to overcome.

Helen, my wife, concurred in my decision, but before making it final I thought it wise to seek impartial advice. The first two whom I consulted, the rector of the church we belonged to and President Henry Wriston of Brown, were strongly opposed. President Wriston thought that I would be making a great mistake to sacrifice my career in classics for anything so nebulous as the Alexander Technique. He knew about Matthias Alexander and his curative powers. (He did not tell me how he knew.) There had always been "healers" of this kind, he said, who by force of their personality could produce miraculous cures. They were never able to pass on this ability to anyone else, however, and the secret always died with them. He did not think I was the kind of person who could work miraculous cures and advised me to stick to Greek. The minister gave me much the same advice and so did several other people. Their arguments did not convince me, however; I had not experienced a miraculous cure but a steady increase in health, which was associated with an increase in knowledge. The knowledge was based on kinaesthetic experiences that I had had and they had not—experiences that at the time I was not able to communicate, though I wanted to do so.

In this dilemma I wrote to John Dewey. It was Dewey's introductions to Alexander's first three books that had given me the confidence to have lessons in the first place. The last of these had been written in 1932, however, and I wondered if Dewey still subscribed to the opinion he had then expressed. He wrote back at once assuring me that he did and approving my decision to take the training course.

I also got support from an unexpected source. Harold Schlosberg, a tough-minded experimental psychologist, was a colleague of mine in the dean's office where we both worked part-time as student counsellors. When an undergraduate at Princeton, Schlosberg had contracted a form of rheumatoid arthritis which left him with limited motion in his joints and complete ankylosis of the upper spine so that the position of his head was fixed. He was subject to severe muscle spasm and was in pain most of the time. Though he was greatly gifted for teaching and research, the amount of time he could devote to either was limited drastically by fatigue. He wore a heavy corset and spent his summer vacations in a private sanatorium resting up for the school year. At my suggestion he investigated the Alexander Technique and found after a series of lessons (in which both of the Alexanders worked with him at the start) that he could dispense with the corset and the sanatorium and teach through the summer as well as the winter. He prized the Technique as a means, the only means he knew anything about, for controlling muscle spasm, and encouraged me to take the training course (he had even considered taking it himself) so that there would be someone in New England to give lessons after the Alexanders were gone.

Having the approval of Dewey and Schlosberg made it easier for me to carry out my decision. It was a three-year course and I agreed that I would not attempt to teach until I had completed it. F. M. agreed that I could take the course at my own pace (during 1941–42 I kept my job at Brown) and that should he return to England before completing it I could finish it with A. R.

9

The Alexander Training Course

There is very little point in reading the best, or most scientific, or most modern, or most medieval books, unless the reader is provided with a technique that permits his Self to implement in psycho-physical practice the ideals set forth in those volumes.

Aldous Huxley

THE WHITNEY HOMESTEAD, on the outskirts of Stow, Massachusetts, was a rambling Victorian house of white frame with a broad veranda across the front. At the back of the house a wide ell had been built on with a modern kitchen and a large, sunny dining room, which could be used as a school room. At the left of the front door a suite of small rooms led to F. M.'s office. Most of the bedrooms were on the second floor. On the third floor was a good-sized dormitory with small open cubicles arranged around a wide hall. Across the road a path led to an older house used only in the summer. The Old House was smaller but it had more charm. The rooms were low-ceilinged with white-painted wainscoted walls. In the kitchen was a brick fireplace with a built-in oven for baking bread, and in the basement there was a secret room which fascinated the children in the school. It was said to have been a station on the Underground Railway.

The Alexander School was established in the Whitney Homestead from January 1941 through September 1942. Besides F. M., the children and the three teachers, A. R. came over from time to time, and a succession of F. M.'s private pupils stayed anywhere from a few days to a month. An American boy who was in the school at Stow has written the following memoir of the life there:

I came to Stow as a boarding pupil in June 1941, just after my ninth birthday. The school was known as the Alexander Trust Fund School. The teachers included Miss E. A. M. Goldie, Miss Irene

Stewart and Miss Ethel Webb. Miss Goldie handled most or all of the academic instruction. All three taught the Alexander Technique.

F. M., when he was there, gave group lessons. It seems to me that both adults and children were in the group. The pupils were seated on chairs in a circle. Sometimes in summer we sat outside under a large horse-chestnut tree on the front lawn. F. M. would move from one pupil to another, often leaving one in an uncomfortable position and moving on to the next. I don't remember specifically that he ever abandoned anyone when they were halfway out of a chair but he might have. While he moved around, he talked and entertained us. He talked about American food and American products (both of which he considered inferior) and he told jokes. His lessons were punctuated with an occasional "There you are," which was a sign of approval.

Both F. M. and A. R. had an uncanny ability to tell when a pupil wasn't "thinking" (which meant "giving orders") and they often caught me. It was a difficult exercise in concentration and I often tried unsuccessfully to make it appear that I was thinking without actually doing so. One of the devices to catch you was to lift your leg at the kneecap to see whether it was heavy or light. If you weren't thinking, the only way to avoid getting caught was by a quick shifting of weight to the other leg.

Miss Webb was the only one that I remember who gave "lying down work." Lying down work was much easier because it is harder to pull down from a supine position and furthermore if Miss Webb ever knew you weren't thinking she never let on.

Both F. M. and A. R. addressed male children as "Boy" and used many expressions unknown elsewhere. "You're fixed," for example, meant you were stiff and had abandoned the primary control mechanism. "Pulling down" meant essentially the same thing as being fixed but was considered more serious. I remember noting when I was at Stow that all US mail boxes had the instruction "pull down" on their handles.

When I was there, I remember reading *Julius Caesar, Macbeth, The Merchant of Venice,* and *Twelfth Night.* We sometimes read these plays outside and occasionally F. M. would join us. I can still picture him playing the part of Shylock. Often after dinner he would perform as an actor. With his eyes sparkling, he would entertain everyone.

I don't know what effect Stow had on the other children who were there because I never saw them again. Although the English

children were far from home, English ways were preserved pretty
much intact. We had tea at four and English style meals. At age
nine, I developed an English accent. The country atmosphere and
the air were good and many must have benefited from the intensive exposure to the Alexander Technique. But I was too young to
be able to observe or measure any marked change among the others or myself.

F. M. gave Stow a dynamic atmosphere. His eyes twinkled with
spirit and enthusiasm. My contacts with him were limited but when
I left Stow in September 1942, I was sorry to go because for the 15
months that I was there I had looked on it as my home.

When I began the training course in July 1941, I was the only
student in it. It was conducted informally like a protracted private
lesson in which one or more of F. M.'s assistants took part. At this
stage I was not allowed to use my hands on anyone else on the ground
that until my use was better I would only be extending wrong habit
patterns into the teaching situation and would give anyone I worked
with wrong experiences. A large share of my time was taken up with
the preparation of a paper on the rôle of the classics in the emancipation of women in nineteenth-century England. In this Miss Webb
proved an unexpected aid. She herself was an "emancipated woman"
and could remember the excitement when in 1887 Agnata Frances
Ramsey alone in her class had won the highest honours in the classical tripos at Cambridge, a distinction that no male student had ever
obtained. It was a great day for women, Miss Webb said.

During that summer F. M. received a disturbing letter from
Aldous Huxley. Huxley was then living in southern California and
had become enthusiastic about the Bates Method of eye exercises.
Mrs. Corbett, his teacher, was being sued in the Los Angeles court
by a group of oculists or ophthalmologists for practising medicine
without a license. Huxley planned to testify on her behalf and was
trying to rally other unorthodox practitioners to her support. F. M.
did not consider himself an unorthodox practitioner and dismissed
the Bates Method as another form of end-gaining. He wrote back
expostulating with Huxley for deserting the means-whereby principle in favour of "beastly exercises."

After I returned to Brown that fall I was asked to review *The
Universal Constant* and *Man's Supreme Inheritance* for the Providence

Sunday Journal. When F. M. heard that I was to do it, he wrote characteristically: "Don't spare me where I deserve a shaking up. I can take it." He seemed to be pleased with what I did, for he ordered two thousand copies for himself and A. R. F. M. was delighted that Huxley had been asked to review the books for the *Saturday Review of Literature.* He had been told in advance that it was "a splendid review." And indeed it was. Huxley seemed to have taken F. M.'s admonishments to heart, for he warned the readers that though "bad symptoms may be palliated by direct methods and a measure of partial good achieved, these results are always obtained at a high price." Huxley's theme in the review was the futility of preaching, "one of the major professions and one of the commonest of hobbies." What effect does all this preaching have, first on the preachers and second on the preached to? Precious little, Huxley thought. The trouble, he said, was that the moralists have always ignored the problem of how the change is to be made, "the problem of bridging the gap between idealistic theory and actual practice." Up to the present only two solutions have been found: the technique of the mystics and the technique discovered by F. M. Alexander. Alexander's technique for mastering "the primary control of the organism as a whole" can be combined "in the most fruitful way," Huxley said, "with the technique of the mystics for transcending personality," so that it is now possible to design a new type of education that would cover the whole range of human activity.

Alexander had reason to be pleased with Huxley's review, for it was widely read and brought him many new pupils. A short while later, however, when Huxley's *The Art of Seeing* appeared, his earlier fears were confirmed. He concluded that the Bates exercises and other end-gaining pursuits had impaired Huxley's general condition and his judgement as well.

By now I was committed to the training course. I attended as many sessions as I could during the winter, and in the spring, right after the Brown commencement, Helen and I put our furniture in storage, and with our two younger children (their older brother was already in the school) we moved to Stow.

Helen joined the course at this point, raising the number of students to two but not changing the character of F. M.'s teaching, which remained unstructured and informal. I started reading some of John Dewey's books and worked the material I gleaned from them into a paper on Dewey and Alexander. My knowledge of the two men was limited and some of the statements now strike me as naïve. Both Dewey and Alexander approved of it, however, and it was published in *School and Society*. As before, the Alexanders ordered two thousand copies. They used to hand out reprints of articles written about the Technique. It was their only form of advertising.

There were more private pupils than the year before, and the rooms in both of the houses were usually filled. Harold Schlosberg was there for a week and Lulie Westfeldt came up from New York for a refresher course. For various reasons, however, the numbers in the Trust Fund School had dwindled, and by September 1942 only four children remained. F. M. decided to close the school and give up the Homestead. A. R. would continue the training course in Boston and F. M. would take over all of the New York practice.

In late September we moved from Stow to Chestnut Hill and I began going in daily to the Braemore Hotel in Boston where A. R. was now conducting the training course. There were four in the class besides myself and Helen: Richard M. Gummere, Jr., who taught at Milton Academy, Mary Macnair-Scott, Alison Grant-Morris and Philomene Dailey. Since the class was larger than the class at Stow, there was more general conversation, which A. R. attempted, not always successfully, to keep on topics related to the Technique. Like F. M. he would not allow any of us to use our hands in teaching until we were "ready." He was vague as to when that would be.

In the course of the year F. M. became increasingly dissatisfied with his life in America. The sales of his book had proved disappointing and pupils were not being attracted to the Technique as they had on his earlier visits. Now that the danger of imminent invasion was over he believed that he could be more usefully employed in England, where his work was not only needed but was better appreciated. This was a belief shared by Sir Stafford Cripps, the Chancellor of the Exchequer, who arranged for a special priority so that the books could be kept in print throughout the war. Early in June 1943, F. M. and his three teachers left on the *Capetown Castle*, a troopship so fast that it did not need an escort.

Before returning they had established a connection with a group of American Friends led by Esther Duke of Swarthmore, Pennsylvania, who felt a "concern" for bringing the Technique into the Quaker school system. Always alert to an opportunity for extending the knowledge of his work, F. M. sent Irene Stewart and Margaret Goldie to Philadelphia to investigate the prospects. They brought back an encouraging report and Irene Stewart began going once a week to Philadelphia to give private lessons while Margaret Goldie set up a small demonstration class at the Media Friends School. When Mrs. Duke realized that F. M. and his teachers would be leaving at the end of the school year, she came to Boston to persuade A. R. to carry on the work in the Philadelphia area, offering to supply him with as many pupils as he wanted. A. R. hesitated for some time, being reluctant to leave Boston, where he had taught since the early 1920s. Finally convinced that it was in the interest of "the work," he moved to Swarthmore in September, followed by all of the students in the training course except Mary Macnair-Scott, who returned to England.

Margaret Goldie's class at the Media Friends School was taken over by Philomene Dailey. The training course was re-established in Swarthmore and I began using my hands to work with the other students. A. R. did not give much specific instruction in the use of the hands, believing that the important thing was to be able to observe both yourself and the pupil and to work out your own style of teaching without end-gaining for specific changes. While you were working with someone, he would glance over from time to time and tell you if you were "pulling down," but he never told you exactly where or how to place your hands. This disturbed me at first, but I believe now that he was right, since I was forced to develop an understanding of the Alexander principle that I could communicate in my own terms instead of taking over a reasonably accurate facsimile of the Alexanders' way of teaching. Fortunately, I have always been able to discuss teaching problems with Helen and work out practical solutions for them.

As I look back on the training course as it was taught by both Alexanders, my strongest criticism would be that it had poor organization. After the two or three hours of class time, everything was turned over to "growth and development." Although the Technique is non-end-gaining, it has to be applied in an end-gaining world. We were given no help in finding ways to bridge the gap. Toward the end of the course I took a part-time job teaching English in an army programme at the Pennsylvania Military College. This constituted just enough stress (I had never taught English before) to create a series of real-life problems which the Alexander Technique helped me to solve. If I had done something like this sooner, it would, I feel sure, have speeded the learning process. (It is a nice question, of course, to decide what constitutes the right amount of stress. Too much would be equally bad. You cannot learn the Technique by crowding it into an already full schedule.)

I completed the training course at the end of June 1944 and received a certificate that was signed, "F. M. Alexander per A. R. Alexander," since unlike the others I had begun the course with F. M. At the end of August, A. R. suffered a stroke, a pretty severe one, it seemed, for he was almost completely incapacitated for a time. He refused to go to a hospital, however. During the fall he regained much of his strength and soon was teaching again. His hands had lost none of their skill, though they had lost some of their strength and he could not move around very much. The lessons he gave me at this time were the best I had ever had from him. This may have been partly because I had improved in myself, but the principle reason was, I believe, that he used less strength to get his effects. One of the basic principles of the Technique seems to be that the amount of kinaesthetic information conveyed is in indirect proportion to the force used in conveying it.

A. R.'s stroke was a blow to me, for I had expected to have his help when I began teaching. His plan had been to have one assistant teacher in Philadelphia, one in New York and one in Boston, and to spend ten days himself in each city every month. I was to be in Boston. The plan had to be given up because A. R. could no longer travel. During the winter I did some practice teaching in Media and Swarthmore, some of it under A. R.'s supervision, and I continued to have as many lessons from him as I could. In June 1945 I came to Boston and taught at Mrs. Codman's until I found teaching rooms for myself on Marlborough Street.

I never saw A. R. again. During the summer of 1945 he went back to England intending to return to Swarthmore or New York. Because of his physical condition, however, he could not obtain a return visa. His advice to me about teaching had always been: "Go slowly and stick to principle." In his last letter he repeated it: "Don't trouble yourself about going slowly," he said; "it is necessary to go slowly." Early in 1947 he suffered a coronary thrombosis and died.

10

Trial in Johannesburg

The past few years have completely altered the foundations of our previous ways of life, and it has become a matter of prime necessity to re-examine the pedigree of all such ideas, conceptions, and beliefs with which our overt activities are associated.

F. M. Alexander, 1946

I OWE A GREAT MANY of the seventy-seven letters I received from F. M. Alexander to the two large boxes of tea that were left in New York when he returned to London in 1943. After the Normandy landings when the sea lanes to England had been reopened, F. M. wrote asking to have the boxes sent to him along with the school books and miscellaneous household goods that had been stored at Stow. The major problem was the tea, which was covered by strict import regulations in England and (as I discovered some time later) by export restrictions in the United States. It took over two years and required the active intervention of Sir Stafford Cripps in London and Christian Herter in Washington, before I succeeded in dispatching the two boxes. F. M. wrote frequently to inquire about my progress and to suggest ways for speeding it up. He felt particularly frustrated by the American regulation, which seemed to him perversely unjust, there being no shortage of tea in the United States. It was "utterly in contradiction," he wrote, "of the principle of liberty and justice." His letters to me were not confined to the subject of tea, however, but were filled with news of his work and of life in England. He was generous with comments and advice, and in response to my questions about teaching, he often gave me helpful suggestions.

Shortly after V-E Day he wrote: "I have been taking all kinds of people who have taken part in this war and I could tell you much that may surprise you, but it is all too long and complex for a letter.

I may put it into a book if I ever get the time to finish another book. At the moment I have a great deal of matter put down, but almost daily I see difficult points clearer and clearer and this means rewriting."

F. M. never finished another book, but he put some of his ideas into an essay that was published in 1946 as an introduction to the British edition of *The Universal Constant in Living* and reprinted in a collection of articles on the Technique edited by Dr. Wilfred Barlow under the title *Knowing How to Stop*. To Alexander the dilemma that had been dramatically thrust before the world by the explosion of the first atomic bomb was the predictable outcome of the split between conscious and subconscious behaviour that marked the condition of civilized man. He believed that man's power over external nature and his ability to exploit this power for destructive purposes was increasing at an accelerated rate unaccompanied by any increase in the knowledge of "*how to control nature within himself*—that is to say, how to control his own reactions to the external world." In an age that demands the highest degree of rational and responsible behaviour, modern man is still controlled primarily by instinct and impulse and "rarely fails to react according to pattern, no matter what the circumstances." Alexander hoped that the bomb had so dramatized the danger that the whole world faces that men would be forced to come to a full stop and realize that their only salvation lay in pushing the boundaries of human evolution further by "bridging the gulf between consciousness and subconsciousness in the control of reaction." Knowing how to stop, he said, demands a technique of inhibition in which refusal to give consent to habitual (subconscious) reaction is the basic means for change. It is the only reliable means by which man can overcome the effects of "emotional gusts" which show themselves in "prejudices, jealousy, greed, envy, hatred and the like," and which ruin the chances for establishing the essential conditions for peace and goodwill in the world.

In addition to Alexander's foreword, *Knowing How to Stop* contained seven articles. Four were by doctors who commented favourably on various aspects of the Technique from the medical point of view. Lest the reader be left with the impression that medical opinion of the Technique was unanimously favourable, the editor added an appendix in which he answered some of the typical objections that had been made to the Technique by other doctors. The three articles that he chose for comment had been written by doctors, none of whom had had lessons in the Technique nor appeared to have read Alexander's books with any care, since they all accused him of claiming to cure disease.

The most prominent of the critics whom Dr. Barlow answered was Dr. Ernst Jokl, who attacked Alexander and his associates in *Volkskragte* (*Manpower*), an official journal of the South African Government. Dr. Jokl was a German physician and physical educator and an authority on exercise physiology. He moved to South Africa in 1933, becoming head of the department of physical education at the Technical College and later the physical-education officer for the South African Government. In 1935 Irene Tasker came to Johannesburg from London and soon established a large practice teaching the Alexander Technique. Among her enthusiastic pupils were Raymond Dart, then professor of anatomy at the University of Witwatersrand, and many other prominent South Africans. Miss Tasker had always specialized in the teaching of children, and her success with difficult cases of emotional disturbance and other kinds of learning disability soon attracted the attention of educators. Dr. Jokl and Miss Tasker met for the first time in June 1941. In the following year he asked her for a demonstration of the Technique and for a course of lessons. Miss Tasker invited him to a group demonstration, but after talking with him she refused to take him as a pupil on the ground that any lessons would be useless "unless preceded by an intellectual acceptance of the principle." She suggested that if he really wanted lessons he should see F. M. himself.

Miss Tasker's caution was undoubtedly wise. Though Dr. Jokl wrote her a flattering letter ("certainly feel that your system means a highly important contribution in the field of education in its widest sense") to others he wrote that he wished "to expose the Alexander Technique and attack the racket" and that he planned to write a small book "in view of the interest which a certain type of pseudo-intellectuals are taking in this peculiar semi-religious movement." Dr. Jokl and his colleague, Dr. E. H. Cluver, director of the South African Institute for Medical Research and a co-editor of *Volkskragte*, had been greatly disturbed to hear that there was a movement to introduce the Alexander Technique in the schools of South Africa, presumably replacing the orthodox system of physical education. Dr. Cluver thought that this was "a most shocking proposal" and "a very serious threat to the health of school children." His fears reached a climax early in 1943, when Mr. I. G. Griffith, president of the Transvaal Teachers Association, in his address to the annual conference praised Alexander's system at great length and dismissed physical-culture, deep-breathing and relaxation exercises as virtually worthless. "Even a very small acquaintance with the Alexander Technique," he said, "causes serious doubts concerning the wisdom of teaching physical training to our children. In this subject we make the children perform movements and exercises completely unrelated to anything they do in school or at any other time. For one hour a week we make the children go through these peculiar and artificial movements and for the remaining 167 hours in the week no one attempts to relate these movements to anything that the children do. In fact, no one cares what sort of movements they perform during that longer period. Physical training exercises are specific, aimed at developing a certain muscle or a certain set of muscles and at perfecting the use of these. If a bad manner of use exists, and it exists in almost every person, that same bad manner of use will be employed to perform these specific exercises and these latter cannot therefore bring about any improvement in the psycho-physical organism. It is true that physical exercises do sometimes bring about a temporary improvement, but inevitably they bring about other effects which are worse than the original ones."

Dr. Cluver thought something should be done at once to defend "the young science of physical education" from this attack, and persuaded Dr. Jokl to write a strong rebuttal for *Volkskragte*. Though reluctant to do it (so he later asserted), Dr. Jokl produced a scathing editorial entitled "Quackery *versus* Physical Education." Referring to Alexander as an "Australian immortal," an "Australian gym master," and an "Australian actor who advertises a system of postural gymnastics of his own design," Dr. Jokl compared him unfavourably to Bernarr MacFadden, Mary Baker Eddy and African witch doctors. "Mr. Alexander's books," he said, "do not contain a single medical case history from which one could learn what all his boast of curing diseased people is about." Jokl was particularly contemptuous of Alexander's doctrine of "conscious control" and "primary control of the individual." Alexander maintains, he said, that "this legendary 'primary control,' if properly brought into play, enables man to subject not only all his muscular actions but also the work of his internal organs to the supervision of his will." He also accused Alexander of claiming to cure cancer and acute appendicitis.

Dr. Jokl's contempt for Alexander extended to all of his followers, who were variously described as prejudiced, irrational, emotional, mentally unstable, and "at least some of them . . . prepared to go to any length to suppress the truth." He dismissed as valueless the testimony of Aldous Huxley because he was not a scientist, of Dewey because he was too old (his "fame as a philosopher and educationalist is, of course, based on writings published when he was younger"), and of Coghill because "he has not produced any evidence in support of the Australian's claims." As for the two British doctors who had attempted to give scientific status to the Technique, their efforts were valueless: "Dr. Murdoch has merely looked at a picture in a book and a specimen in an anatomical showcase [and] drawn conclusions," while Dr. Douglas's paper is "devoid of scientific value."

Jokl's article was brought to F. M.'s attention in August 1944. He made no reference to it in any of the numerous letters I received from him in that year and the next (this was at the height of the tea correspondence), and it was not until two years later that I learned from Ethel Webb that he had decided to bring suit for defamation. F. M. was not a stranger to litigation. Twenty years earlier, by threatening to sue an author and his publisher, he had forced the withdrawal of a book describing a system of re-education suspiciously like his own. But this time the author was a doctor in a position of power and the publisher was the South African Government. Most of F. M.'s friends thought it would be wiser and more in keeping with the means-whereby principle to ignore the attack. They pointed out that libel cases are seldom decided on the main issue (which in this case was whether experience can be trusted if it is obtained through unorthodox channels) and are apt to be decided on some false issue (which in this case was likely to be whether the Alexander Technique could cure disease). Alexander, however, was angered by the personal character of the attack and the fact that it had been directed against him in wartime by a German. He decided that his work should be defended, and in August 1945 after the editors had refused to with draw the article he brought an action against them for five thousand pounds damages in the Rand Division of the Supreme Court of South Africa.

When the case finally came to trial two and a half years later, it had become a *cause célèbre*. (It is referred to in South African legal circles as "the famous Alexander case.") From February 16 to March 1, 1948, the courtroom in Johannesburg was filled to capacity, with a queue waiting patiently outside in the hope that some of the standing room might be vacated. The Johannesburg *Star* devoted a full page to the trial for each of the twelve days the court was in session; and the transcript of the evidence ran to 450,000 words.

The case was tried before Mr. Justice Clayden, with O. Pirow K.C. and M. van Hulsteyn appearing for defendants, and H. J. Hansen K.C. and A. Fischer for the plaintiff. The defendants chose to rest their case, which was prepared for them in the office of the Government attorney, on the testimony of experts who had had no experience of the Technique but who were prepared to say there was nothing in it. As soon as the suit was filed Dr. Jokl went to London to get support and was "inundated," he said, with offers from doctors and physiologists eager to testify against Alexander. Evidence was taken at South Africa House from such distinguished scientists as Sir Henry Dale, Lord Adrian, Professor Samson Wright and Sir Alfred Webb-Johnson. None had met Alexander or had lessons in the Technique, but all claimed to have read the books (Professor Wright said that he made "a careful and unbiased study" of them) and all dismissed them with contempt—"pretentious verbiage," Sir Henry Dale called them. Lord Adrian said that "Alexander's claim that the researches of Magnus supported his teaching was unfounded"; and all the physiologists ridiculed the idea that Alexander's "primary control" had anything to do with the *Zentralapparat* which Magnus had so brilliantly demonstrated. The experts singled out for special condemnation Alexander's doctrine of conscious control, which they described in almost identical language as "complete conscious control of every function of the body." Since Alexander had nowhere advocated such a control but had expressly rejected it as undesirable and dangerous, it is hard to tell where the description came from. The strongest statement for the defence was made by Professor Wright, who pointed out that Alexander did not have the physiological knowledge necessary to inspire trust in his statements, and on the other hand had given no records of case histories or other data that would "permit an impartial person to examine and judge for himself the value of his assertions." Consequently, he said, "one must treat with the utmost scepticism any claims that [he] makes." Like the others, he had seen no reason for investigating them further.

To counter the evidence of the physiologists, the lawyers for Alexander produced a letter from the *British Medical Journal* signed by nineteen doctors who said they had observed beneficial changes in the patients they had sent to Alexander. Alexander's lawyers also obtained statements made expressly for the trial by four practising physicians who strongly endorsed the Technique. The most impressive and probably the most influential evidence obtained in London for Alexander was the statements of two laymen, Sir Stafford Cripps and Lord Lytton. Sir Stafford said that he considered that a wider knowledge of Alexander's writings and methods was "of the very greatest importance to the future welfare of the country." He denied that he was a partisan for Alexander but admitted that he was "a great partisan for Mr. Alexander's technique, . . . because I believe it to be something of great value to the human race. I should feel very guilty if I did not." Sir Stafford considered that Jokl's article had libelled him personally, implying that in supporting Alexander "he was either a fool or a knave."

Lord Lytton, who had met Alexander when governor of Bengal, said that he had benefited greatly from the lessons he had had from him. He admitted that the books were difficult to read and that he himself did not altogether understand them. He thought, however, that Alexander's work was very important and that he had consented to be a trustee of the fund set up to support an Alexander school. "I had failed to get from his books," he said, "what I got from his treatment, and as what I got from his treatment seemed to me of enormous value I was very anxious that what I regard as his sound treatment should not perish with him." Lord Lytton said that Alexander had never to his knowledge claimed to cure specific diseases.

Though almost seventy-nine, Alexander had a heavier teaching schedule than ever and the preparation of the case was making greater demands upon him financially and emotionally than he had anticipated. In November 1947 Miss Webb wrote: "It has been a hateful experience for him to listen to some of the evidence that has been taken privately in London against him by medical men who don't know him or his work. The whole thing has been a 'knock' for him and he looks older and worn by it." In December he had a bad fall followed a week later by a stroke, which left him partially paralysed. He had planned to testify in person and had booked passage for Capetown, but on his doctor's orders the trip to South Africa was cancelled and the trial began without him.

In reply to the charge of defamation Messrs. Pirow and van Hulsteyn presented a double defence. They denied that the article if read as a whole had any of the meanings alleged by the plaintiff; alternatively they pleaded that it was true in substance and was in the public interest. The first part of the defence was dropped, however, after Mr. Hansen for the plaintiff read selections from Dr. Jokl's article.

Mr. Hansen began his case by calling two medical witnesses, Dr. Wilfred Barlow and Dr. Dorothy Drew, who had flown in from London to testify. Both gave their evidence in a straightforward fashion. After stating their medical qualifications they said that they had studied the Technique, had benefited from their knowledge of it, and had advised their patients to have lessons. Dr. Barlow, a specialist in physical medicine, described the Alexander Technique as "re-education in body mechanics" and cited medical authorities for the importance of good body mechanics to health. He considered that the Alexander Technique was the best method for achieving it. On cross-examination, Mr. Pirow asked: "Would you send an acute appendicitis case to Mr. Alexander for cure, as he claims?" Dr. Barlow replied that people, whether they were sent by doctors or not, went to Alexander for education and not for cure.

When they testified for themselves, the defendants did not hold up as well under cross-examination as had Dr. Barlow and Dr. Drew. They overstated their case against Alexander, misrepresented his teachings and misquoted his writings. The way in which they charged all of Miss Tasker's supporters with being neurotics gave the impression of vindictive malice. Dr. Jokl, for example, admitted that when Professor Dart had published a letter defending the Technique he had attempted to have Dart's name struck off the roll of the Medical Council. He explained that the flattering note he had written Miss

Tasker after the demonstration she gave him was meant in the same spirit as "telling a lady at a party 'what a beautiful green frock yours is' when I don't mean it is very beautiful at all." Dr. Cluver said that such terms as "Australian actor" (which had been used in a pejorative sense more than twenty times in the article) were meant only "to show the background of the man." In calling Alexander's teaching "pernicious" he merely wished to protect the health of the school-children. Dr. Cluver admitted that he himself had written a book in which he said that man's instincts were not adequate to cope with recent changes in his environment and that education was essential but denied that this was in any way similar to Alexander's teachings. In the same book he had said, "Unless our lives are joyous we run the risk of getting alimentary cancer or thrombosis." Mr. Hansen asked if there was not a danger that someone with a pain in his stomach might after reading his book decide to be joyous instead of seeing a doctor and would risk getting a burst appendix. Dr. Cluver said the implications were ridiculous; upon which Mr. Hansen suggested that they were equally ridiculous in Mr. Alexander's case.

A trump card that Mr. Hansen introduced into the record was a letter to Alexander from Sir Charles Sherrington. In his latest book, *The Endeavour of Jean Fernel* (1946), Sherrington had said: "Mr. Alexander has done a service to the subject by insistently treating each act as involving the whole integrated individual, the whole psycho-physical man. To take a step is an affair not of this or that limb solely but of the total neuromuscular activity of the moment—not least of the head and neck." Alexander wrote him a letter of thanks, to which Sherrington replied: "I need not repeat to you that I appreciate the value of your teaching and observations. I was glad to take occasion to say so in print. I know some of the difficulties which attach to putting your ideas across to those less versed in the study than yourself. Your disciples, however, can more and more disseminate them and multiply your call." Sherrington concluded the letter with a direct reference to the pending suit in South Africa: "I am sorry you should be worried by a scurrilous attack. A German is, of course, liable to be violent and rude."

Sherrington's statements were a severe blow to the defendants. The physiologists who had testified on their behalf in London were eminent but not so eminent as Sir Charles. Dr. Jokl explained the letter as "one of conventional kindness from a very great and kindly man" (like his own letter to Miss Tasker). Sherrington, he said, had told him personally that he considered Alexander a dangerous quack and that if he had not been a cripple and ninety years old he would have gone to give evidence against him. Dr. Cluver disposed of Sherrington's tribute as "that of a kind man but undeserved." When he was asked if Sherrington had ever made an appreciative reference to any other quack, he was forced to say no.

At the end of the cross-examination Dr. Jokl admitted that Alexander was quite convinced he had something marvellous to give the world. "What I wanted him to produce in support of his claims," he said, "was case histories and other evidence of scientific value."

In his closing argument Mr. Pirow said that Alexander was an ignorant layman with very little knowledge of anatomy or physiology who claimed nevertheless to have special healing and therapeutic powers. His books were useless as guides to health and without value as expressions of a meaningful philosophy of life. As to his presumptuous claim that his work was scientific, that could be decided only by men of science and they were overwhelmingly against him. Anyone who was for him "suffered from some form of anxiety neurosis."

On the other side Mr. Hansen argued that Dr. Jokl's article had misrepresented Alexander's teachings by omitting all reference to his principle of re-education and to the rôle of inhibition in his system. The real theme of the article was the fear that the Alexander Technique might someday supplant the orthodox form of physical education in the schools. Hansen admitted that Alexander had not gathered all the objective proof that would be needed to establish his findings as a scientific principle, but that in no way invalidated them. "The concept that man should be treated as a psycho-physical whole, that the mind and the emotions have an important bearing on health and disease may be as old as the hills, but Mr. Alexander's claim from its practical application in his technique is new; and the value of that technique has not in my submission been disproved. On the contrary the evidence of pupils strongly supports the claims."

The verdict, which was given on April 20 by Mr. Justice Clayden, was in favour of the plaintiff. The decision was a forty-nine-page document that analysed pro and con the 450,000 words of testimony put in evidence during the trial. In his summary Judge Clayden paid tribute to the expert evidence for the defence but pointed out that it was directed chiefly to proving the falsity of claims that Alexander had never made and was "designed rather to support Dr. Jokl's article than to deal with the effects of Mr. Alexander's technique in practice. . . . The defendants have in my view to prove not only that the system as described is unsound but that as described and in operation it is unsound. They have to prove . . . that persons who have undergone a course of instruction from Mr. Alexander or his teachers do not thereafter have improved body mechanics. Since none of the defendants' witnesses have seen such a person this is difficult. . . . They have shown that Mr. Alexander supports his technique by wrong physiological reasoning and by reference to work which almost certainly has nothing to do with it. But that in my view is not enough. . . . They have failed in my view to prove that the system cannot bring about the results which it does claim in the improvement of health and the prevention of disease, and again they have made matters worse by overstating the claims made for the system. The claim to improve health has not been shown to be baseless even in the medical field."

Ordered to pay damages of one thousand pounds with costs running into five figures, the defendants chose to appeal the case. The appeal was not heard until the following year (1949) when it was unanimously rejected on June 3 by the three-man court. In pronouncing his judgment that the article was defamatory, Chief Justice Watermeyer said that the "plaintiff was entitled to compensation for his injured feelings and the hurt to his dignity and reputation, including not only his good name from a moral and social point of view but also a teacher of his system of psycho-physical education."

Though the money Alexander received did not cover all the expenses he had incurred, the verdict was a tremendous relief to him and a great source of satisfaction. In December he wrote me: "All goes well with the work here and we are busy in the preparation of the evidence in the legal action for early publication. It will be a very interesting document and will do much to do away with the myth that because a man has been appointed to an important position his judgement is better than that of other men." Although this document was never published, the London newspapers gave good coverage to the case and summaries appeared in *The Lancet*, the *British Medical Journal* and the *South African Law Reports.*

Alexander was now over eighty. He had recovered from the stroke and was making gradual progress, he wrote, in the matter of health and strength and increasing his working hours "much to the surprise of my medical friends." Apropos of the improvement in his health he copied out a passage for me from Sherrington's "Notes on Reflex Inhibition": "There is no evidence that inhibition is ever accompanied by the slightest damage to the tissue; on the contrary it seems *to predispose the tissue to a greater functional activity thereafter.*" This, Alexander wrote, "is a most important confirmation of the value of the primary activity of inhibition in the carrying out of the means-whereby of the technique."

11

Dewey and Alexander

The crucial educational problem is that of procuring the postponement of immediate action upon desire until observation and judgement have intervened.

John Dewey, *Experience and Education*

No thinker can ply his occupation save as he is lured and rewarded by total, integral experiences that are intrinsically worth while. Without them he would be completely at a loss in distinguishing real thought from the spurious article.

John Dewey, *Art as Experience*

THE JUDGMENT AGAINST the editors of *Volkskragte* was a victory for Alexander but only half a victory for the Alexander Technique. It was established legally that Dr. Jokl's article was defamatory and that he had not shown Alexander's claim to be false. The trial could not, of course, establish the Technique scientifically, and Dr. Jokl's demand for "at least the physical equivalents of the great mental experience" remained unanswered.

After the trial Alexander's medical supporters continued to write articles about the Technique. The most productive of them was Dr. Wilfred Barlow (1947, 1952, 1954), who brought some of Alexander's procedures into the field of physical medicine as a superior form of posture training. For postural re-education, Barlow recommended a conditioning procedure "first described by Alexander" in which the subject is taught to associate (by means of a Pavlovian mechanism—"a Konorski Type 2 reflex") a sequence of verbal orders (which he vocalizes at first and then gives to himself subvocally) with "an improved disposition of the body and its tensional balance," produced by manipulation. Dr. Barlow (1954) demonstrated the re-education procedure with a group of fifty students from a London voice and drama college, and reported an improvement for all of them. Changes in twenty were assessed by means of somatotype photographs taken before and after training. Speaking as a physician, Dr. Barlow said he had found the Alexander procedures useful "in such varying conditions as peptic ulcer, spastic colon, ulcerative colitis, eczema and rheumatoid arthritis" as well as "tension headaches, asthma, low back pain and fibrositis."

Barlow's articles proved of little help when I tried to explain the Technique to Boston doctors. They were not impressed by the before-and-after photographs or the list of diseases to which the Technique had been applied. By this time I was beginning to realize that the Alexander Technique could not (and probably should not) be established in a medical frame of reference. Since the principle was preventive rather than curative, there did not seem to be much point in collecting and recounting case histories, no matter how impressive the changes. Doctors could always find some other way to explain them. I reluctantly came to this conclusion after I succeeded in teaching a badly crippled girl of seventeen to walk. She had had Still's disease at nine months; her legs were like pipestems; and she could move around only by swinging herself on crutches. She learned how to walk, first with the help of her crutches and then without them. The learning took place in a large hospital and the process was observed by four doctors and several nurses. Everyone was pleased with the results. They explained them, however, by saying that I had used suggestion to restore the girl's confidence in herself. The experience convinced me that a clinical study of the Technique would be of little value until the principle it rested on had been demonstrated experimentally, and it could be shown that the clinical results followed from the means employed and could not be attributed to some other mechanism like suggestion.

The problem of obtaining experimental evidence for the Alexander Technique was one to which John Dewey had given a great deal of thought, and the opportunities that I had to discuss it with him were invaluable to me. Though I had had some correspondence with Dewey, I did not meet him until June 1947, when I called on him in New York. He and Roberta Grant had been married the winter before and were living with their two adopted children in a large, cheerful,

Courtesy of Irene Tasker

Fig. 2. John Dewey and F. M. Alexander

old-fashioned apartment on upper Fifth Avenue. The Deweys were hospitable, informal and easy to talk to; and the feeling of awe with which I arrived was soon dissipated. Dewey had been reading an article in the *Psychological Review*. As I came in he threw it down with an impatient gesture, remarking, "I despair of psychologists. They seem to think that borrowing a technique from another science makes them scientists." He pointed to the cracks in the plastered wall behind me and said, "If I measured each of those cracks, I could calculate their slopes and derive a formula for them. That would not be science, but I could fool a psychologist into thinking it was." Almost the only example of scientific method in a field of psychology today, he said, was the Ames demonstration in visual perception. He was greatly distressed that foundation support had been suddenly withdrawn from the Dartmouth Eye Institute, where Ames had done his experiments.

I asked Dewey about his early experiences with the Alexander Technique. He said that he had been taken by it first because it provided a demonstration of the unity of mind and body. He thought that the demonstration had struck him more forcibly than it might have struck someone who got the sensory experience easily and quickly, because he was such a slow learner. He had always been physically awkward, he said, and performed all actions too quickly and impulsively and without thought. "Thought" in his case was saved for "mental" activity, which had always been easy for him. (Alexander told me that when Dewey first came to him he was "drugged with thinking" and used to fall asleep during lessons.) It was a revelation to discover that thought could be applied with equal advantage to everyday movements.

The greatest benefit he got from lessons, Dewey said, was the ability to stop and think before acting. Physically, he noted an improvement first in his vision and then in breathing. Before he had lessons, his ribs had been very rigid. Now they had a marked elasticity which doctors still commented on, though he was close to eighty-eight.

Intellectually, Dewey said, he found it much easier, after he had studied the Technique, to hold a philosophical position calmly once he had taken it or to change it if new evidence came up warranting a change. He contrasted his own attitude with the rigidity of other academic thinkers who adopt a position early in their careers and then use their intellects to defend it indefinitely.

I asked him if he thought the Technique had implications for the moral as well as the intellectual side of life, and he agreed emphatically that it had. In his own case, he said that once he had decided on a course of action as the right one to follow, the Technique made it much easier for him to carry it out. In the introduction to *The Use of the Self* he spoke of "the great change in mental and moral attitude that takes place as proper coordinations are established," and in a letter to me he said that these aspects of the Technique were "an intrinsic part of the whole scheme." Irene Tasker told me that when she first went to South Africa Dewey had given her a letter of recommendation in which he spoke of her teaching as "contributing to the physical, mental and moral improvement of the child."

In the face of Dewey's positive statements about the moral and intellectual value of the Technique, I have always found it difficult to understand the insistence by his disciples that its application was purely physical—as if the Technique were a kind of Australian folk remedy which Dewey in the kindness of his heart had endorsed in order to help Alexander sell his books. I ran into this attitude long before I met Dewey. Sidney Hook had given a lecture at Brown on some aspect of Dewey's philosophy. I had just discovered Alexander's books and had been impressed by Dewey's introductions to them. At the end of the lecture I went up to the platform to ask Hook about Alexander's influence on Dewey. He looked at me uncomprehendingly at first and then said with obvious embarrassment: "Oh yes! Alexander was an Australian doctor who helped Dewey once when he had a stiff neck." A little later in an article on Dewey in the *Atlantic Monthly* Max Eastman described Alexander as "A very unconventional physician . . . an Australian of original but uncultivated mind." "Dewey was smiled at in some circles," Eastman wrote, "for his adherence to this amateur art of healing but it undoubtedly worked in his case." In Corliss Lamont's *Dialogue on John Dewey*, Alexander again appears as a quaint character who was "concerned with your posture and that sort of thing." The speakers agreed that "Dewey thought Alexander had done him a lot of good," but none of them gave Dewey credit for intelligent judgement, and Ernest Nagel (according to Horace Kallen) attributed the whole episode to superstition on the part of Dewey. This picture of Dewey as the naïve supporter of an ignorant Australian doctor has unfortunately been given increased currency in a recent biography, *The Life and Mind of John Dewey*, by George Dykhuizen (1973).

Having tried in vain to discover the reason for the discrepancy between Dewey's own testimony about his relations with Alexander and the testimony of his disciples, I came to the conclusion that "there were no reasons only causes" (as A. E. Housman said of the persistence of errors in classical scholarship). A serious investigation of the causes was made by E. D. McCormack in his doctoral dissertation, *Frederick Matthias Alexander and John Dewey: A Neglected Influence* (1958). Starting out with Dewey's 1939 statement that his "theories of mind-body, of the coordination of the elements of the self and of the place of ideas in inhibition and control of overt action needed contact with the work of F. M. and A. R. Alexander to turn them into realities," McCormack explored the meaning and tested the validity of the statement by the use of new biographical material obtained from letters and interviews and by a comparative analysis of the writings of the two men. One of the conclusions to which he came was that Dewey's endorsement of Alexander's work proved "his deep conviction that Alexander was correct" and that writing off the endorsement as that of a "kind patron lending his approval and influence to the support of just another praiseworthy endeavour" was to impute serious intellectual dishonesty to Dewey (p. 158).

There is no doubt that Dewey was disappointed and hurt that his strong, positive statements about Alexander's principles—for example, that they "bear the same relation to education that education bears to all other human activities"—were mocked or ignored. In November 1942 Miss Webb, who was staying with Mrs. Wendell Bush in New York, wrote me: "Someone was in tonight who knows him and says he is lonely now and is often depressed. . . . It sometimes seems as if his disciples, like the men in the Bible who continually said 'Lord, Lord,' are satisfied to call on his name but don't go on to apply his teaching in what they are doing." When I knew him five years later, he was certainly not lonely, but there was no one with whom he felt able to discuss the Alexander Technique. He apologized for not introducing me to more people, saying that those of his friends who might have been sympathetic to the Technique were dead.

It is easy to see why the lessons appealed to Dewey (apart from their contribution to his health and well-being). They provided him with a kind of laboratory demonstration of principles that he had arrived at by reasoning: the aesthetic quality of all experience; the unity of conscious and unconscious; the continuity between self and environment; the operational significance of inhibition; the indivisibility of time and space. All of these concepts had theoretical validity for Dewey, but the concrete, sensory evidence that lessons supplied gave them a solid grounding in experience. Alexander, Dewey said, was the only person he knew or knew of "who knows what he is talking about in the way a competent engineer knows when he is talking about his specialty" (McCormack, p. 129). The reason Dewey continued to study the Technique long after it had "made him over" physically was that the lessons kept enlarging and sharpening his experiences. "As one goes on," he wrote in *The Use of the Self*, "new areas are opened, new possibilities are seen and then realized; one finds himself continually growing, and realizes that there is an end-less process of growth initiated."

Passages could be collected from almost any of Dewey's later books that reflect his experiences with the Alexander Technique. In two of them, *Human Nature and Conduct* (1922) and *Experience and Nature* (1925), Alexander is referred to explicitly.

Human Nature and Conduct was expanded from three lectures given at Stanford University in June 1918. Part One is devoted to the place of habit in conduct. Habit in Dewey's exposition is interactional ("transactional" was the term he later preferred). Like breathing and other physiological functions, habits, though learned rather than innate, involve a relation between an organism and an environment and cannot be understood by looking at the organism alone. What is true of physical habits is also true of morality. Virtues and vices, moral functions like cowardice or courage, do not belong exclusively to a self but have meaning only by reference to an environment. Because of their interactional nature, habits, like physiological func-tions, "can be studied objectively and can be modified by change of either personal or social elements."

Habits are not "an untied bundle" of isolated acts. They inter-act with one another and together make up an integrated whole. Whether or not a particular habit is manifest, it is always operative and contributes to character and personality. "A man may give him-self away in a look or a gesture," said Dewey, anticipating the body-language people. "Character can be read through the medium of individual acts."

Mechanization is an essential property of all habit. But it does not follow that habit must be mindless. "The real opposition," Dewey said, "is not between reason and habit, but between routine, unintelligent habit and intelligent habit or art." Habit can be plas-tic and creative. Indeed, in a changing world it must be: "Old habits must perforce need modification no matter how good they have been." It is the function of intelligence to determine where changes should be made.

A habit cannot be changed, however, without intelligent control of an appropriate means or mechanism. To believe that it can is to believe in magic. People still think, nevertheless, that by passing laws, or by persuasion, by "wishing hard enough" or "feeling strongly enough" they can change human behaviour and get a desirable result. That, Dewey says, is superstition. At this point in the argument he introduces F. M. Alexander and devotes the next fifteen pages to an exposition of the Alexander Technique as a scientific and reliable means for changing habitual behaviour.

> Recently a friend remarked to me that there was one superstition current among even cultivated persons. They suppose that if one is told what to do, if the right *end* is pointed to them, all that is required in order to bring about the right act is will or wish on the part of the one who is to act. . . . He pointed out that this belief is on a par with primitive magic in its neglect of attention to the means which are involved in reaching an end. And he went on to say that the prevalence of this belief, starting with false notions about the control of the body and extending it to control of mind and character, is the greatest bar to intelligent social progress. . . .
>
> We may cite this illustration of the real nature of a physical aim or order and its execution in its contrast with the current false notion. A man who has a bad habitual posture tells himself, or is told, to stand up straight. If he is interested and responds, he braces himself, goes through certain movements, and it is assumed that the desired result is substantially attained. . . . Consider the assumptions which are here made. It is implied that the means or effective conditions of the realization of a purpose exist independently of established habit and even that they may be set in motion in opposition to habit. It is assumed that the means are there, so that the failure to stand erect is wholly a matter of failure of purpose and desire. . . .
>
> Now in fact a man who *can* stand properly does so, and only a man who can, does. In the former case, fiats of will are unnecessary, and in the latter useless. A man who does not stand properly forms a habit of standing improperly, a positive, forceful habit. The common implication that his mistake is merely negative, that he is simply failing to do the right thing, and that the failure can be made good by an order of will is absurd. . . . Conditions have been formed for producing a bad result, and the bad result will occur as long as the bad conditions exist. . . . It is as reasonable to expect a fire to go out when it is ordered to stop burning as to suppose that a man can stand straight in consequence of a direct action of thought and desire. The fire can be put out only by changing

objective conditions; it is the same with rectification of bad posture.

Of course something happens when a man acts upon his idea of standing straight. For a little while, he stands differently, but only a different kind of badly. He then takes the unaccustomed feeling which accompanies his unusual stand as evidence that he is now standing right. But there are many ways of standing badly, and he has simply shifted his usual way to a compensatory bad way at some opposite extreme. . . . Only when a man can already perform an act of standing straight does he know what it is like to have a right posture and only then can he summon the idea required for proper execution. The act must come before the thought, and a habit before an ability to evoke the thought at will. Ordinary psychology reverses the actual state of affairs. [pp. 27–30]

Dewey uses this example of "standing straight" to illustrate his general law of habit: "Only the man whose habits are already good can know what the good is." McCormack in his commentary on this passage says that through Alexander, Dewey as a philosopher "has suddenly experienced what the Gestaltists call 'closure.' . . . One might say that a Copernican Revolution has taken place as a result: thought now revolves around habit, instead of habit around thought as hitherto and in 'ordinary psychology' " (pp. 98–99). Dewey is convinced that experience must come first and concepts evolve from it. But if concepts have become linked to wrong, maladaptive experiences, how is change possible? Dewey found the answer in Alexandrian inhibition. We must give up the idea of gaining the end (that is standing up straight) directly, and approach it indirectly "through a flank movement."

We must stop even thinking of standing up straight. To think of it is fatal, for it commits us to the operation of an established habit of standing wrong. We must find an act within our power which is disconnected from any thought about standing. We must start to do another thing which on one side inhibits our falling into the customary bad position and on the other side is the beginning of a series of acts which may lead into the correct posture. The hard drinker who keeps thinking of not drinking is doing what he can to initiate the acts which lead to drinking. He is starting with the stimulus to the habit. . . .

Until one takes intermediate acts seriously enough to treat them as ends, one wastes one's time in any effort at change of habits. Of the intermediate acts, the most important is the *next* one. The first or earliest means is the most important *end* to discover. . . .

We must change *what* is to be done into a *how*, the means whereby. The *end* thus re-appears as a series of "what nexts," and the what next of chief importance is the one nearest the present state of the one acting. Only as the end is converted into means is it definitely conceived, or intellectually defined, to say nothing of being executable. . . . Aladdin with his lamp could dispense with translating ends into means, but no one else can do so. [pp. 35–37]

Dewey's account of the Alexander Technique is close to the account in *Man's Supreme Inheritance*, though it is, of course, much more succinct. It leaves out the sensory experience that is given to the pupil by the teacher and that makes it easier for the pupil to alter his incorrect concept of the end he wishes to attain. It describes the inhibitory act as if it could be worked out by the pupil independently (as, indeed, it had been by Alexander himself). And there is no reference to the "primary control," a concept that was not developed until later. It is nevertheless a remarkable exposition of Alexander's principles, and the whole chapter can profitably be read as a philosophical introduction to the Technique.

Experience and Nature (1925), which Dykhuizen says is generally considered Dewey's magnum opus, is an enlarged version of the Paul Carus lectures given in 1922. Dewey had again been having lessons in the Technique and their influence is again apparent. "Of all Dewey's published writings," McCormack said, "*Experience and Nature* is the one in which Alexander's principles stand out most clearly and have penetrated most deeply." There is no detailed account of them as in *Human Nature and Conduct*, but anyone who has studied the Technique himself can perceive its effect on the tone and often on the language of almost every chapter. In particular, Dewey's discussions of the mind-body problem, the rôle of inhibition, the continuity between man and nature, the immediate felt quality of things, the degeneration of the civilized subconscious, the perversion of sensory appreciation, and the need for controlling the process of change all reflect his experiences in studying with the Alexanders. McCormack, applying a kind of "litmus test" of idiomatic terms and phrases for detecting Alexander's influence, came to the conclusion that *Experience and Nature* could not be fully understood without knowing what Alexander taught.

Dewey studied the Alexander Technique intermittently through-out the 1920s and 1930s. From 1935 to 1941, he was having lessons with A. R. Alexander, and he told me that in many respects he got more from them than from the lessons he had from F. M. Applying the litmus test to books written during this period—*Art as Experience, The Quest for Certainty*, the revised edition of *How We Think, The Theory of Valuation, Experience and Education*—provides the Alexander student with a wealth of passages that evoke experiences he has had in applying the Technique to his own life.

Dewey staked his reputation on the scientific character of the Alexander Technique, stating positively and unequivocally that "Mr. Alexander's teaching is scientific in the strictest sense of the word." McCormack says that in the introduction to *Constructive Conscious Control*, "Dewey expresses his position on these and related matters with such vigour that one is at pains to know why this essay has been neglected." In it Dewey discusses what scientific method is and what it isn't, reiterating the five steps (first set forth in *How We Think*, 1910) by which problems are solved scientifically. He concluded the discussion by saying:

> After studying over a period of years Mr. Alexander's method in actual operation, I would stake myself upon the fact that he has applied to our ideas and beliefs about ourselves and about our acts exactly the same method of experimentation and of production of new sensory observations, as tests and means of developing thought, that have been the source of all progress in the physical sciences. . . . [xxvii]

Alexander's principle was scientific because it was demonstrable; it had "falsifiability," to use Popper's term. It could only be demon-strated, however, to someone who was willing to have lessons in the Technique. As Dewey said in *The Quest for Certainty* (1947): "One may lead a horse to water but cannot compel him to drink. If one is unable to perform an indicated operation or declines to do so, he will not of course get its meaning." Unfortunately, very few, even of Dewey's own disciples, would allow themselves to be led to water, let alone drink.

Since the Technique could not be demonstrated without the cooperation of the Alexanders, Dewey found himself in a dilemma. He recognized that "the first requirement of scientific procedure is full publicity as to material and processes" (*Theory of Valuation*, p. 22). He wanted an investigation in which modern scientific techniques would be used to provide objective evidence for Alexander's "primary control of use." Alexander, however, could not see any advantage in such an investigation. He was convinced that recognition would ultimately come, and in the meantime, as McCormack put it, "he had a comfortable monopoly in the teaching of his technique." This attitude was exasperating to Dewey. A scientific investigation, he wrote me, was something that Alexander "was never able to undertake because of early obstinate prejudices—whose formation or persistence is readily understandable on any theory except his own."

My own attitude at this time coincided with Dewey's. It was increasingly frustrating for me that I was unable to produce any objective evidence for a principle that my senses told me was true and my experience convinced me was of fundamental importance. I did not consider myself qualified by temperament or training to undertake a scientific investigation, but no one else seemed prepared to undertake one and I found myself gradually propelled in that direction. In the fall of 1949 one of Alexander's pupils who had recovered from a serious heart condition gave me five hundred dollars for research. I decided to spend it on a pilot study of electromyography (which seemed a promising place to begin) and arranged to do it at the Tufts Institute for Applied Experimental Psychology, which was then under the direction of Dr. John Kennedy. The results of the first venture were very modest, but when I wrote Dewey about them he was delighted. He wrote back, "You have every good reason to be pleased to the point of excitement," and advised me to seek foundation support. He died before I succeeded in getting it. I often wished in the course of my investigation that I could have discussed it with Dewey. Without his encouragement I might never have undertaken it.

12

Experimental Studies

In conjecturing what may be, men set before them the examples of what has been, and divine of the new with an imagination preoccupied and coloured by the old; which way of forming opinions is very fallacious; for streams that are drawn from the springhead of nature do not always run in the old channels.

Francis Bacon, *Novum Organum*, CIX

A SCIENTIFIC INVESTIGATION of the Alexander Technique was easier to talk about than to implement. Funds would be needed to support it and a laboratory to conduct it in. I did not have access to either, and my use of scientific method had up to then been confined to the study of Greek participles. Fortunately I had pupils who could make up for some of my deficiencies. At this time I was giving lessons to psychologist Harold Schlosberg (my former colleague at Brown), and Grayson McCouch, a physiologist. Schlosberg was then engaged in his revision of Woodworth's classical textbook in experimental psychology and was thoroughly versed in experimental methods that had been successfully applied to the study of sensorimotor phenomena. Dr. Grayson McCouch was professor of neurophysiology at the University of Pennsylvania Medical School. He had worked with both Sherrington and Magnus and had made important contributions of his own to the literature on the postural reflexes. Neither was willing to undertake an investigation of the Technique himself, but both were happy to share with me their special knowledge and experience in research. They suggested background reading, introduced me to other researchers, answered questions, criticized what I wrote, and saved me from saying something that was "unphysiological" or "psychologically naïve."

Another person whose help was invaluable at this time was Dr. Arlie Bock, director of Student Health at Harvard and professor of hygiene at the Harvard Medical School. He had learned of the Technique from patients of his who had studied with me, but his curiosity was finally aroused by a student who wrote him that twenty lessons in the Alexander Technique had done more for him "physically" than the hundreds of hours of "physical education" he had received at Harvard and Exeter. The student suggested that Dr. Bock sponsor an experimental programme "in some special postural training class, where results would probably be most clear and so most useful; or as an alternative to a callisthenics program. . . . I feel sure myself," he added, "that the simplicity and effectiveness of the Alexander Technique would soon show it to be preferable in many cases to other methods relying on 'treatments' or 'exercises.' " Dr. Bock was keenly interested in research himself (he had been the director of the Harvard Fatigue Laboratory), and after looking into the Alexander Technique he decided that it should be investigated scientifically. He was unable to get anything done at Harvard since he was on the point of retiring, but he arranged to have a study made at the Massachusetts General Hospital in which I would collaborate with Dr. Stanley Cobb, chief of psychiatry. Dr. Cobb was interested in the study and proposed fifteen questions which were "probably answerable by a not too complicated investigation." Greatly encouraged to have gained the interest and support of so eminent a researcher, I prepared to go ahead with the investigation under Dr. Cobb's direction but learned at the last minute that it had been vetoed by some higher authority at the hospital. At this point, through the good offices of Drs. Bock and McCouch, I was introduced to research-oriented doctors at the Harvard Medical School who were sympathetic with my aims and generously allowed me to attend the lectures and demonstrations in anatomy and physiology which helped me to acquire enough basic knowledge in the two areas to read technical books and articles critically.

About this time I received from a pupil, whose blood pressure, after thirty years of hypertension, had come down to normal, another five-hundred-dollar gift for research. I spent it on a second pilot study at the Institute for Applied Experimental Psychology at Tufts University. The most important outcome was the discovery that multiple-image photography could be used to demonstrate the effect of the Technique on patterns of movement. The study led ultimately to my appointment at Tufts as Research Associate and a little later as Lecturer in Classics.

The Institute for Applied Experimental Psychology (later the Institute for Psychological Research) was probably the only place in the country where a Greek scholar could feel welcome in a psychological laboratory. Established in 1945 by Leonard Carmichael to handle sponsored research (usually government research) in the field of human engineering, it was organized in such a way that members of the psychology department automatically became members of the institute but members of the institute were not necessarily members of the department. Mason Crook, the scientific director, set the tone for the institute. A brilliant and original investigator himself, he seemed to have no difficulty in co-operating with a non-psychologist, and the rest of my new colleagues followed his lead. This was fortunate for me, since I needed all the advice and assistance I could get.

With the multiple-image photographs and the electromyograms from the two pilot studies I felt that I had enough objective data to approach one of the foundations. I was turned down by the Rockefeller Foundation, but Professor J. McVicker Hunt, whose wife had studied the Technique with A. R. Alexander, gave me an introduction to John Gardner at the Carnegie Corporation of New York, and I succeeded in obtaining one of the small grants they used for encouraging research in new, unsupported areas. The Carnegie grant led to support from the US Public Health Service for seven years. When the support was discontinued, I accepted a professorship in classics at Tufts, but continued my research on a smaller scale through government contracts and with the help of gifts from pupils and friends.

In launching an investigation the first thing that had to be done was to define the problem in operational terms so that it could be attacked experimentally. There were two approaches that could be taken: 1) to measure changes in performance, appearance and personality that take place over a period of time and after an appreciable number of lessons; 2) to study the physiological correlates of the kinaesthetic effects that can be produced in a single lesson.

Schlosberg favoured the first approach since it would be easy to design a series of experiments along conventional lines, using control groups and a set of performance tests to measure progress. The same objection holds, however, as for a clinical study. Until the mechanism is understood, positive results can always be explained by appeal to some extraneous principle like strength of motivation. Negative results, on the other hand, might signify only that the subject had failed to learn the Technique or was not employing it in the re-test. Though this type of experiment was not ruled out, it seemed wiser to defer it until more was known about the phenomenon and then to do it on a larger scale than was then contemplated.

The second approach seemed more promising. By using the procedures described in Chapter 2, the pattern of an habitual movement can be changed very quickly. Most subjects use similar language in reporting the kinaesthetic experiences that are elicited by the change. It should be possible, I thought, to study these experiences scientifically like any other sensory experience. In studying visual and auditory perception it is customary to correlate the subject's report with an objective record of the stimulus pattern that elicited the report. Brightness discrimination, for example, could be studied by presenting two lights and asking the subject to judge whether the degree of brightness was the same or different, and, if different, to estimate the degree of difference according to some predefined scale. An objective measure of brightness (for example, in candle-power) would be obtained simultaneously. Similarly, for the discrimination of sound, two musical notes could be presented to a subject whose task would be to report whether or not they differed in pitch, loudness or timbre. To adapt the method to kinaesthetic perception, the subject would be asked to make judgements of differences in the feeling of a movement when performed under different conditions. What was lacking was a simple way of recording the movement so that differences could be measured objectively and correlated with differences in the subjective report. Multiple-image photography seemed to be the method most likely to give the kind of records we needed.

MULTIPLE-IMAGE PHOTOGRAPHY

Multiple-image photography was a precursor of the motion picture. It was developed by Etienne Marey, the French physiologist, in the 1880s. Marey, who was interested in the analysis of human and animal movement, discovered that by leaving the shutter of his camera open and interrupting the light at fixed intervals with a perforated disc (a "Marey wheel") rotated in front of the camera he could record a movement as a succession of discrete images whose time relations were known. He refined the method for the study of human movement by dressing his subject in black clothing and attaching metal reflectors at various places on the head, trunk and limbs. In the photographs, which were taken in strong sunlight against a dark background, the image of the subject disappeared, leaving only a black-and-white pattern showing the successive positions of the markers. Marey called this method "geometric chronophotography."

Marshall Narva and I had used a Marey wheel in combination with small electric lights fastened to the subject and connected by wires to a battery. We found that measurable differences in the patterns would distinguish between "habitual" and "guided" movements. Later, on the advice of Professor Edgerton at MIT, Donald O'Connell and I adapted the method to use with multiple-strobe. Dispensing with the wheel and the electric lights, we attached markers of reflecting tape to the subject (who again was dressed in dark clothing) and took the photographs with a Strobolume which could be flashed at many different rates. Besides giving a gestalt of the movement, the method provides a large number of quantitative indices from the various trajectories. Patterns recorded in this way provide data that can be analysed graphically and statistically.

Four pairs of patterns are reproduced in figures 3 to 6. They show the effect of a change in the head–neck relation in four everyday movements: from lying down to sitting up; from sitting to standing; from leaning forward to sitting up straight; walking. In all of them there is a change in the head trajectory which increases the area underneath the curve. The change is reflected by differences in the patterns made by the other markers. In general the patterns of the guided movements are smoother, more regular, and contain more space.

1. Colour-coded multiple-image photograph of the author walking.

2. Colour-coded multi-beam photograph of fireball-type lightning.

3. Colour-coded multiple-image photograph showing walking up and down stairs. Flash rate: 10 fps.

4. Colour-coded multiple-image of the author descending a staircase.

A

Fig. 3 Multiple-image photographs of the movement from lying down to sitting erect. A. Habitual movement; B. Guided movement. Flash rate: 10 fps.

B

A

B

Fig. 4 Multiple-image photography of the movement from sitting to standing. A. Habitual movement; B. Guided movement. Flash rate: 10 fps.

Fig. 5 Multiple-image photography of the movement from leaning forward to sitting erect: A. Habitual movement; B. Guided movement. Flash rate: 10 fps.

A

B

Fig. 6 Multiple-image photography of walking A. Habitual movement; B. Guided movement. Flash rate: 20 fps.

COLOUR CODING

In many of the patterns the exact time relations between different trajectories cannot be accurately determined, since movement begins at different times in different parts of the body. We solved the problem of time determination by using colour to code the patterns. The idea of colour coding occurred to me when I was watching a display of precision dancing at the Roxy Theatre in New York where spotlights in changing colours picked out individual dancers and followed them through the various routines. To obtain a similar effect we constructed an aluminium disc with five large apertures, each covered with a gelatine filter of a different colour. The disc was made to rotate in synchrony with the strobe at 5, 10, or 20 flashes per second (fps), changing the colour of each successive image so that synchronous parts of the pattern were identified. Examples of colour coding are shown in the colour plates (I-IV).

HABITUAL AND EXPERIMENTAL SITTING POSTURES

The commonest of everyday movements is straightening up from a slump either in sitting or in standing. This is the movement Dewey used to introduce his discussion of habit in *Human Nature and Conduct*. It is a movement that is performed against gravity, and it is regularly associated with a feeling of effort. When the balance of the head is altered by the method I have described, the pattern of the movement changes and the feeling of effort is markedly reduced. Multiple-image photographs of the two movements are shown in figure 7. The camera had been moved close to the subject to bring out the pattern more clearly. A graphical analysis of the head relation in the two patterns was made by measuring the displacements of a point on the head and a point on the trunk and plotting the data from a common origin (figure 8). Similar analyses from twelve other subjects showed considerable variation in the habitual patterns but very little in the experimental.

The line drawings in figure 9 (traced from photographs) show the habitual relaxed posture and two erect postures, the end results

Fig. 7 Multiple-image photography of movement from slump to an erect sitting posture: A. Habitual movement; B. Guided movement.

Fig. 8 Graphical analysis of the movement from a slump to an erect posture shown in fig. 7, showing horizontal and vertical displacements of head (centre of Frankfurt Plane) and neck (7th cervical vertebra). H. Habitual movement; G. Guided movement.

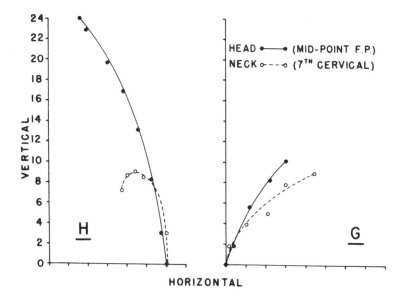

of the two movements from "relaxed" to "erect." In B the subject's head is in virtually the same plane as in A; in C it has rotated slightly forward as it moved up. Note that it is possible to move from A to B and from A to C but not from B to C.

We sought further definition of the three sitting postures by magnitude estimations of effort, surface electromyography and X-ray photography.

Fig. 9 Three sitting postures (traced from photographs). A. Habitual relaxed; B. Habitual erect; C. Guided erect.

TABLE 1

SUBJECTIVE JUDGEMENTS OF EFFORT FOR TWO ERECT SITTING POSTURES

Subject	Habitual Relaxed	Habitual Erect	Experimental Erect
1	10	15	7·5
2	10	30	10
3	10	15	7
4	10	15	7
5	10	13	10
6	10	13	10
7	10	16	6
8	10	15	10
9	10	13	8.5

MAGNITUDE ESTIMATIONS

In all subjects whom we have tested, the "habitual erect" posture represents a marked increase in effort over the "habitual relaxed," whereas the "experimental posture" does not. Data taken from nine subjects who made magnitude estimates of effort (using ten as the standard for habitual relaxed) are given in Table 1 (Jones, 1970). The increase in estimated effort for habitual erect ranged from 30 percent to 300 percent. For the experimental posture, the subjects reported either no increase, or a decrease ranging from 15 percent to 40 percent. These reports have been frequently confirmed in subsequent studies.

ELECTROMYOGRAPHY

Surface electromyography, which in a rough way measures changes in the electrical potential of muscle, will sometimes give an indication of the comparative effort involved in the two erect postures. The sample electromyograms in figure 10 show the activity in six different muscle groups on neck and trunk as the subject moved from a relaxed to an erect posture with and without guidance. In the habitual erect posture there was a marked increase in the activity of the lower trapezius muscle which did not appear when the movement was guided.

The muscles that most sharply and consistently distinguished the two erect postures were the sternomastoids, the V-shaped pair of muscles at the front of the neck. These are the muscles that stand out like ropes on the necks of dancers straining to hold position, or of runners straining to win a race. They can be seen prominently in the forced breathing of asthmatics and in stammerers struggling to speak. We measured their activity in seven subjects (college undergraduates) as they moved from a relaxed to an erect sitting position (Jones, Hanson and Gray, 1961). In all of them, activity increased significantly when they were asked to sit in their "best sitting posture" and further when they sat at their "greatest sitting height." No increase took place in the "experimental" posture or in the movement

Fig. 10 Sample electromyograms from six different muscle groups on neck and trunk. A. Habitual relaxed; B. Habitual erect; C. Guided erect.

Fig. 11 Sample electromyograms showing activity in the right sternomastoid muscle during various sitting postures and during the movement from the most comfortable to an erect sitting posture. MCP, Most comfortable posture; BSP, Best sitting posture (habitual); GSH, Greatest sitting height; Exp, Experimental posture (guided into an erect posture); Mov't H, Habitual movement; Mov't G, Guided movement. The arrow indicates initiation of movement.

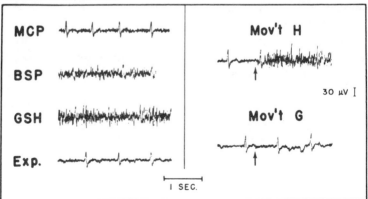

leading into it. A sample record showing raw muscle activity scores is shown in figure 11.

X-RAY PHOTOGRAPHY

To make a careful study of the anatomical distinctions of the three postures, we obtained X-ray photographs of twenty dental students (Jones and Gilley, 1960). An analysis of these revealed several indices which distinguished the experimental posture from the habitual erect at a high degree of significance. The difference between the two postural responses can be clearly seen in the X-ray photographs (from a more recent series) illustrated in figure 12. In figure 12A the subject is shown at left profile sitting in a comfortable relaxed posture. In figure 12B he was asked to sit at his "full height". In figure 12C the movement to the erect posture has been guided by the experimenter. Wire clippings attached to the subject's skin by adhesive tape mark the origin and insertion of the sternomastoid muscle. Measurements taken from the original X-ray photographs show that the distance between the markers is greater in the experimental erect than in the habitual erect posture. The spaces between the vertebrae are greater in the experimental posture and *sella turcica* (a bony landmark which corresponds approximately to the centre of gravity of the head) has moved forward and down.

These changes do not require a particular head position. In a sense, the experimental posture is not a posture at all but a change in the anatomical relationships in the head and neck which can occur in any position. The X-ray photographs illustrated in figure 13 show the same subject asked to look up at a target (45° above eye level) in his habitual manner (13A), and with the guidance of the experimenter (13 B). The pictures show a striking difference between the two postures. The experimental posture is again distinguished by increased intervertebral distance, forward movement of *sella turcica* and greater distance between the markers indicating the length of the sternomastoid muscle.

A

B

C

Fig 12 X-ray photographs showing various sitting postures: A. Relaxed; B. Habitual erect; C. Guided erect. In C there is an increase of 0.8 cm betwen origin and insertion of sternomastoid.

SUBJECTIVE EYE LEVEL

An important index of postural orientation is subjective eye level, the horizontal line that a person identifies as at the level of his own eyes. After lessons in the Alexander Technique pupils frequently comment on the fact that their eyes are resting at a lower level than they are accustomed to. Samuel McLaughlin and I tested the subjective eye level of ten subjects. They were seated in a darkened room and asked to direct the raising or lowering of a luminous bar until it seemed to be at the level of their own eyes. When the subjects moved from their habitual relaxed to their habitual erect posture, the relation between subjective and objective eye level remained virtually the same (that is, as their sitting height increased, they asked to have the bar lifted by about the same amount). When they were guided into the experimental posture, however, the subjective eye level dropped

Fig. 13 X-ray photographs showing subject looking up approximately 45 degrees. A. Habitual; B. Guided. In B, there is an increase of 1.75 cm between origin and insertion of sternomastoid.

A   B

significantly (that is, though their sitting height increased, they asked to have the bar lowered).

The Movement from Sitting to Standing

It is in movement rather than posture that the Alexander Technique is uniquely manifest. The movement we have studied most extensively is the movement from sitting to standing (figure 4). It is a discrete movement in which the body is accelerated and decelerated in a brief span of time (two or three seconds). Well suited to analysis by multiple-image photography, it has a pattern that is characteristic of the individual and changes very little on repetition (Jones and Hanson, 1961, 1962). The pattern changes markedly, however, when the reflex relation of the head to the trunk is altered.

The change of pattern is most striking when the movement is guided by the experimenter (as in figure 6B). It is less striking, but clearly marked nevertheless, when the subject is allowed to stand up by himself (that is, without guidance) after the head relation has been altered (adjusted). The "adjusted" pattern is illustrated in figure 14 where the subject gets up twice in his habitual way and twice after the head–neck–trunk relation has been changed. For all four patterns (which were colour-coded originally) the instructions to the subject were the same: "Stand up when you hear the signal."

The differences in the three types of movement (habitual, adjusted and guided) are brought out by the diagrams in figure 15. The diagrams were constructed by making enlarged prints from the transparencies and using colour to identify and connect synchronous points on head (midpoint of the Frankfurt plane), neck (7th cervical vertebra), chest (sternal notch), and thigh. The series of triangles obtained in this way give an expression of the changing relation between head, neck and trunk at $1/10$-second intervals during the movement.

Similar sit-to-stand patterns were obtained from six subjects (male undergraduates at Tufts University) before and after twenty lessons in the Alexander Technique (Jones, Gray, Hanson and O'Connell, 1959). At each photographic session eight multiple-image photographs were taken. Four of the eight movements were

A

B

Fig 14 Multiple-image photography of sit-to-stand movement patterns: A. and B. Habitual; C. and D. Adjusted. The term *adjusted* indicate that the subject was guided into the starting posture but that the movement itself was not guided. Flash rate: 10 fps.

C

D

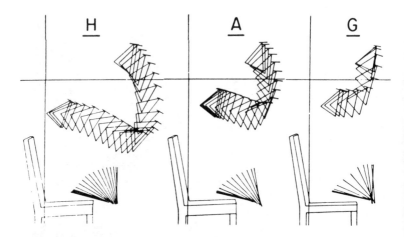

Fig. 15 Triangle diagrams (traced from multiple-image photographs) showing sit-to-stand patterns. H. Habitual; A. Adjusted; G. Guided. (Top of triangle is centre of Frankfurt plane with bar to indicate tilt of head; base of triangle connects 7th cervical vertebra with sternal notch.)

habitual (that is, the subject got up without guidance or adjustment), two were adjusted, and two were guided. For each subject the first two movements were always habitual; the other six were randomized.

From the two photographic sessions ninety-two patterns were obtained for analysis. (Two were lost in each session because of double exposure.) A triangle diagram was constructed for each pattern. These diagrams could be placed by inspection in groups corresponding to the three examples in figure 15. In both series the guided patterns distinguish themselves sharply from the other two. In Series I, the adjusted patterns fall unmistakably between the habitual and the guided. In Series II, however, a change has taken place in the habitual patterns so that they can no longer be distinguished from the adjusted.

The patterns were analyzed graphically and statistically. Linear and angular displacements were measured directly from the prints, and velocities and accelerations were calculated from the displacements. By plotting the data all of these relations can be expressed graphically as functions of time or of each other.

To treat the data statistically we selected such measures as the maxima and minima of various functions, calculated their means and made t-tests of the differences. The functions that made the best criteria for distinguishing among the patterns were: three angles, delta (the angle between head and neck), eta (the angle made by the horizon with a line drawn from the 7th cervical vertebra to the sternal notch), and theta (which measures the forward thrust of the head); rise time (the time it takes the head to rise higher than starting level); trajectory ratio (which measures the extent to which the head trajectory departs from a straight line joining the beginning and end of the movement); the distance of the thigh from the sternal notch at the moment of rise. All of these measures distinguish the habitual from the experimental patterns with a high degree of statistical significance. Three of them, head thrust, rise time and trajectory ratio, were applied to patterns that could be judged "better" or "worse" by some external standard. A group of students classified as "well coordinated" on the basis of standard tests was compared with a "poorly coordinated" group (Jones and Hanson, 1961): and a group of normals was compared with a group of patients suffering from neurological diseases (Jones et al., 1963). The three indices that had distinguished the experimental from habitual movement patterns distinguished (in the same direction) well coordinated from poorly coordinated and normal from abnormal. By these criteria, then, the experimental movements are not only different from the habitual, they are better.

FORCE-PLATFORM MEASURES

A direct measure of the difference in force exerted by the subject in the habitual and experimental movements was provided by a strain-gauge force platform. The force platform is a device for recording shifts in force over time on a polygraph. It consists of a wooden board attached to an aluminium tube on which strain gauges have been mounted (O'Leary, 1970). The polygraph pen is deflected in an amount proportional to the force applied by the subject. The device has been useful as a means of measuring unneeded preliminary shifts in weight due to "postural sets." In one study the subject first sat on a high stool with his feet on the force platform. Then he sat on the platform with his feet on the floor. The force/time curves in figure 16 were recorded while the subject moved from sitting to standing (Jones and Hanson, 1970). In A and D, he gets up in his habitual way; in B, C, E and F the movement is guided by the experimenter. It can be seen that guidance, by eliminating the postural set from the movement, subtracted approximately twenty-five pounds of force which the subject ordinarily used to get the movement started. Similar records have been obtained for the beginning of walking and for climbing stairs.

THE KINAESTHETIC EFFECT

The kinaesthetic effect of lightness and ease of movement is reported by the great majority of subjects. Some observe it immediately, some only after a number of repetitions. Occasionally a subject does not notice any kinaesthetic difference at all. Since suggestion is not only not used but sedulously avoided, it is important in teaching to find

Fig. 16 Force platform records showing force–time characteristics in the sit-to-stand movement. A. Habitual with feet on platform; B. and C. Guided with feet on platform; D. Habitual while seated on platform; E. and F. Guided while seated on platform.

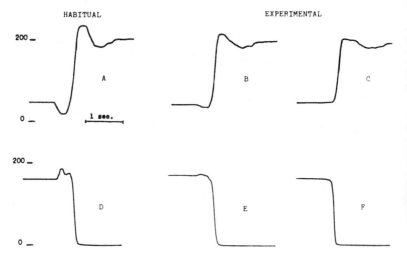

out what kind of experience the pupil is having. To make the task of reporting his feelings easier, we constructed an adjective checklist containing eighteen words, sixteen of them paired opposites. Data were obtained from thirty-nine naïve subjects after a first lesson of ten or fifteen minutes in which every effort was made to avoid verbal suggestions of any kind (Jones, 1965). The data are given in Table 2.

TABLE 2

PERCENTAGE OF RESPONSES OF
39 SUBJECTS TO THE ADJECTIVE CHECK LIST

Adjective	%	*Adjective*	%
Lighter	72	Tenser	20
Less familiar	62	Brighter	15
Higher	59	More difficult	15
Smoother	54	Less steady	13
Slower	44	Heavier	13
More relaxed	44	Faster	10
Easier	41	Jerkier	10
Softer	38	Duller	8
Steadier	36	Lower	3

The four adjectives ("lighter," "less familiar," "higher" and "smoother") that were most frequently chosen correspond to measurable differences in the photographs and the force-platform records. "Smoothness" (which is the opposite of "jerkiness") is a quality of the movement pattern that manifests itself not only in the shape of the trajectory but in the time values as well. All movements start and end at zero velocity. The way in which maximum velocity is reached and sustained—the rate of acceleration—can be either smooth or jerky and felt as such. The difference can be seen in figure 16 in which speed of head movement in a pair of habitual and guided movements is plotted against time (Jones et al., 1959). The guided movement, though it is completed in a shorter time, reaches a lower

Freedom to Change

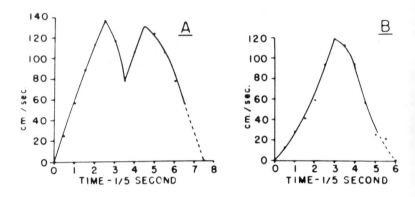

Fig. 17 Speed of head movement in an habitual and a guided movement as a function of time. A. Habitual; B. Guided.

maximum velocity. In the habitual movement there are two maxima,
and the rate of acceleration and deceleration is much steeper.

Despite the feeling of relaxation that many subjects report, we
have not found the consistent changes in heart rate, breathing, brain
waves or the galvanic skin response that have been claimed for the
various techniques of relaxation, self-hypnosis and meditation. The
changes we have found in individual subjects are those associated
with a higher rather than a lower level of activation and seem to
reflect an increase in alertness rather than relaxation as such.

REFLEX RESPONSES

Two movements that the Alexander brothers used in their teaching
were elicited as slow reflexes involving either a shortening or a lengthening response throughout the extensor system. The value of these
procedures as a teaching device may be questioned, since they cannot
be used with everyone and failure to obtain the effect can produce
anxiety. When successful, however, they provide a dramatic demonstration of the reflex character of posture. Harold Schlosberg said it
was like going up and down in an elevator. We recorded both procedures with multiple-image photography.

Reflex Standing: The subject, sitting in the experimental posture, is asked not to alter the balance of his head while the experimenter rests a hand lightly against his back. As the experimenter gradually increases the pressure of his hand in a horizontal direction, the subject equalizes the pressure by coming back instead of going forward as he would ordinarily do in response to such a stimulus. When the pressure reaches a certain level (varying with the distribution of tonus in the subject's back and his ability to inhibit a change in the head–neck relation), the subject will be brought easily and smoothly to his feet. Since his attention is engaged in carrying out the experimenter's instruction, the upward movement will be involuntary and will

Fig. 18 Multiple-image photograph of the reflex-elicited movement from sitting to standing. Flash rate: 10 fps.

come as a surprise the first time it is elicited. In the pattern reproduced in figure 18, the straight line of the head trajectory shows that the two horizontal forces were evenly balanced. (If the subject is standing, the same procedure will bring him up onto his toes.)

Reflex Sitting. The movement from standing to sitting can also be elicited as a slow reflex. The effect of the sudden application of pressure to the back of the knees is well known (it was first described in Homer's *Iliad*). If the pressure is applied slowly and smoothly while the subject's attention is engaged in inhibiting a change in the head–neck relation, extensor muscles will lengthen without loss of tonus and bring the subject by a smooth, easy movement into the chair. The reflex movement is illustrated by the multiple-image photograph in figure 19B. (The reflex movement pattern may be contrasted with that of the voluntary movement in figure 19A.)

The Startle Pattern: Another "total reflex" that involves the relation between head and trunk is the "startle pattern," the stereotyped postural response to a sudden loud noise. Recorded photographi-

Fig. 19 Multiple-image photographs of the movement from standing to sitting. A. Habitual; B. Reflex.

A   B

Fig 20 The startle pattern. A. Best standing posture; B. Posture
following startle stimulus. Electromyograms of the upper trapezius
(above) and the sternomastoid (below) are also shown.

cally, it provides a vivid example of how "good" posture can change to "bad" posture in a very brief time (figure 20). In A the subject, a high-school athlete, is standing in his "most comfortable" posture. Markers similar to the markers used in the multiple-image photographs have been attached to the head, neck, chest and thigh. Surface electrodes over the right sternomastoid and right upper trapezium record changes in muscle potential. In 20B the subject has been startled by the sudden slamming of a door. The two sets of neck muscles have contracted simultaneously, thrusting the head forward but keeping the Frankfurt plane horizontal. The postural change does not stop with the head and neck. The shoulders are lifted and the arms extended, the chest is flattened, and the knees are flexed. The change, which is not instantaneous, begins in the head and neck, passing down the trunk and legs to be completed in about a half a second.

John Kennedy and I studied the pattern with multiple-channel electromyography (Jones and Kennedy, 1951). We placed surface

Fig. 21 Electromyographic activity associated with the startle pattern. From top to bottom are the neck, shoulder, back, abdomen, thigh and calf. Arrow indicates onset of startle stimulus.

electrodes in various locations, always having one pair over the upper trapezium. The intensity of the stimulus varied from the sound of a dropped book to the sound of a .32-calibre revolver. The sample pattern reproduced in figure 21 shows how the pattern spreads from neck to leg. Sixty patterns were obtained from eight different subjects. Whenever the stimulus was strong enough to elicit a response, it appeared in the neck muscles; in many cases it appeared nowhere else.

The startle pattern contains elements of extension as well as flexion. Landis and Hunt (1939), who studied the pattern with high-speed cinematography, were uncertain which element came first but decided that it must be flexion. We tested the theory with the force platform (Jones, unpublished data). When a person stands on the platform, a sudden flexion sends the polygraph pen down (as it would send the pointer down if he were standing on a scale) whereas sudden extension of the body sends it up. Six subjects were startled by the sound of a .32-calibre starter's pistol as they stood on the platform. In every trial the first movement of the pen was always upward, then downward. Apparently the response begins with extension.

READING AND WRITING

Head displacement is a useful index for measuring postural change as a response to stimuli, whether the response is sudden and transitory as it is in the startle pattern or gradual and protracted as in old age and disease. Two of the most powerful stimuli for producing malposture are a book and a pencil. Their effect can be observed by visiting any schoolroom. Using head displacement as an index, Helen R. Jones (1965) measured the effect of reading and writing on the postural patterns of thirty-eight children in the third grade of an elementary school. Each child was photographed in right profile as he sat in a straight chair. A horizontal marker of narrow black tape was placed high on the right cheek between the eye and the ear. The child's own self-concept of "good posture" was used as a standard for the first photograph. Photographs were then taken as the child looked at a standard eye chart twenty feet away; at a small eye chart two feet away; as he read from a familiar book; as he read from an unfamiliar book; as he wrote his name with a pencil. The child was then guided into the experimental posture, and additional photographs were taken as he sat comfortably, read from the small eye chart, and wrote his name. To treat the data statistically, the vertical, horizontal and angular displacements of the head marker were measured for each of the postures. Means and standard deviations for 38 subjects were calculated from the measurements.

The results showed that engaging in writing consistently produced a dramatic deterioration of posture as reflected in a forward and downward displacement and an exaggerated forward tilt of the head. The reading tasks had a similar effect, causing the head to be displaced forward (especially in the case of the near eye chart) and downward. When the subjects had been guided into the experimental posture, the strength of the reading and writing stimuli was effectively diminished and the children were able to engage in reading and writing with postures as good or better than their standard erect postures.

Fig. 22 Writing postures. A. Habitual; B. Guided.

A   B

The most important outcome of the study was the discovery of how quickly and easily a postural change can be made in a child of this age. The change usually manifested itself within a minute or two by a spontaneous smile. The child's reading was not disturbed by the change, though the distance between his eyes and the chart increased. In most of the children the character of the writing changed markedly, presumably reflecting a difference in the use of the hand and arm. A pair of photographs in figure 22 shows the difference in writing behaviour.

SKILLED PERFORMANCE

What can be done with everyday movements can also be done with skilled performance. Marjorie Barstow in Lincoln, Nebraska, has had extensive experience with musicians and dancers. She likes to demonstrate the Technique by making an immediate change in an individual's performance. I have been able to make similar changes both with singers and with instrumentalists, which are recognized by both the performer and the listener as an improvement.

In seeking ways to record these changes we have experimented with a number of methods. For musicians (cellists and pianists) we have recorded the sounds on tape and compared the habitual with the experimental performance. Figure 23 shows how head balance in a singer can be changed during performance. The same song was recorded on a tape recorder, before and after the change. The singer reported greater ease and greater resonance in her voice and better control of her breathing in the experimental condition, and her judgement was confirmed by other musicians. Corresponding sections of the tape, recording the end of one phrase and the beginning of the next, together with the interval in which a breath was taken, were sent to a voice-print laboratory for analysis. The sound spectrograms in figure 24 show the increase in the overtones and the virtual disappearance of breathing sounds after the balance of the head was changed.

Musicians frequently report that with the Technique they have greater control over timing and rhythm. We obtained a visual record

Fig. 23 Head balance in a singer. A. Habitual; B. Balance altered by experimenter.

Fig. 24 Sound spectrograms associated with the two head balances shown in fig. 23. A. Habitual; B. Balance adjusted by experimenter.

of these differences in a conga drummer by placing the drum on the force platform and recording the performance on the physiograph.

F. M. died when the Tufts study was just beginning. He had given cautious approval to the first reports I made, but his attitude in general was that there was no need to investigate the Technique itself, since that had already been done by him. From my point of view, however, the study had been invaluable. It proved to my satisfaction that the subjective phenomenon that I had set out to investigate (the sensory effect of lightness) could be reproduced under controlled conditions, was reported in similar terms by independent observers, and possessed a set of physical dimensions corresponding to subjective reports of the experience. Though only a pilot study, it had produced methods for obtaining the objective data that would be needed to develop a testable theory of mechanism. With such a theory and with a reliable set of standards for judging a pupil's progress in learning to use the Technique, a full-scale investigation, clinical as well as experimental, becomes possible.

13

What is the Mechanism?

*. . . we understand by "mechanism" whatever checks or controls
and guides into determinate paths the workings of energy.*
        D'Arcy W. Thompson, *Of Growth and Form*

*The extraspective and the introspective methods of observation
have equal scientific validity and both methods are subject to the
hazards of erroneous interpretation.*
        C. Judson Herrick, *The Evolution of Human Nature*

IN ADVANCING HIS revolutionary doctrine of the circulation of the
blood, William Harvey described an experiment he had performed
upon himself. He had examined the veins of his forearm and
observed that the blood could be stripped from whole sections by
running a pressed finger along the vein in the direction of the hand
and that the vein would remain empty of blood until the pressure of
the finger was removed. If, however, the finger was pressed along the
vein in the other direction (away from the hand), the vein remained
full. The results of this experiment (which anyone could repeat) were
consistent only, Harvey argued, with the view that the blood circu-
lates, passing out from the pumping heart through the arteries and
returning through the veins. Harvey did not rest his proof on this
demonstration alone but went on to give a detailed and lucid account
of the anatomical and physiological mechanisms that confirmed his
theory.

Alexander's doctrine of inhibition and primary control lends
itself to the same kind of demonstration and proof. (Alexander's first
discovery came from visually observing the effect of stress on the axis
of his head.) The Technique, however, extends the scope of self-
observation a long way beyond the visual by organizing the kinaes-

thetic sense on a conscious level. Once you can observe changing relations between parts of the body and between the body and the environment in terms of levels of tension and relaxation, of lightness and heaviness, as well as of position and movement, you have opened new areas of the self to scientific exploration. By itself, sensory evidence is not enough. It must be supported by anatomical and physiological reasoning. On the other hand, reasoning alone is not enough either. No matter how well a theory is constructed, it does not become valid until it has been put to the test of experience—to sensory verification.

My strongest impression when A. R. Alexander first demonstrated the Technique to me was that of a mechanism working against gravity. I could not see what A. R. had done, but I could perceive its effect on me. I was occupying more space; my movements were less jerky; and I had lost my customary feeling of heaviness. Whatever his procedures were, they had made a radical change in my relation to the gravitational field. The change was not an illusion, since the sensory effect lasted for the rest of the day. It was a new experience which I had neither learned nor willed. There must, I thought, be a mechanism or set of mechanisms already present—a physiological *a priori*, to use Magnus's term—to account for the effect.

In its relations with human beings gravity has generally had a bad name. It is commonly thought of as a hostile force which has to be fought against and overcome. Part of the fascination of the space programme lies in the opportunity it offers to television viewers of vicariously escaping from the pull of gravity. One of the most eloquent expressions of this feeling about gravity was made by the biologist, D'Arcy W. Thompson. In his great book, *On Growth and Form*, he wrote:

> Man's slow decline in stature is a sign of the unequal contest between our bodily powers and the unchanging force of gravity which draws us down when we would fain rise up. We strive against it all our days, in every movement of our limbs, in every beat of our hearts. Gravity makes a difference to a man's height, and no slight one, between the morning and the evening; it leaves its mark in sagging wrinkles, drooping mouth and hanging breasts; it is the indomitable force which defeats us in the end, which lays us on our death bed and lowers us to the grave.

This lamentation had always appealed to me for its compassionate picture of humanity oppressed by gravitational force. Now I had had a striking demonstration that the picture was wrong. I had not been oppressed by gravity but by my ignorance of the rôle it played in posture and movement. If it were the indomitable force that Thompson described, it is hard to imagine how man could have achieved the upright posture in the first place, or for that matter how the animals could have come up out of the sea. Obviously a mechanism to neutralize the effects of gravity must always have existed as long as there was life on earth. Obviously such a mechanism would be inherited and the use of it would not be a matter for effort or learning. And obviously the laws governing its use would apply to man as well as to the other animals. Obvious as these facts now appeared, they had not occurred to me before I had the experience I have described.

There are three major aspects of the anti-gravity response which are important for understanding the phenomena I have been describing: the rigid strength of bone and the elastic strength of ligaments; the hydraulic force exerted by the spongy cartilaginous discs between the vertebrae and by the synovial fluid in the joints; the versatility of muscle which, through its connection with the nervous system, can make a variety of responses to the same stimulus.

BONES AND LIGAMENTS

Because of their rigidity and strength, bones give a necessary stability to posture. They also contribute through their weight by supplying the necessary stretch to maintain tone in muscles and ligaments. Ligaments are bands and sheets of tough, fibrous tissue which bind bones together and resist rotational pulls. Besides strength they possess resilience and elasticity. They can be stretched within certain limits, but when the stretching force is released they will return to their former size and shape. They help to support the head, to strengthen the spinal column, to suspend the arms, to stabilize the joints of the hips, knees and ankles, and to give resilience to the feet. If allowed to function properly, they contribute to the stability of posture and the smoothness of movement.

INTERVERTEBRAL DISCS

D'Arcy Thompson spoke of the difference in a man's height between morning and evening. The difference, which is frequently observed, can amount to as much as an inch or more. In the 1930s a Budapest physician named DePuky measured the heights of 1,216 persons aged five to ninety just before they got into bed at night and just after they got up in the morning. The average increase from night to morning was 1.6 cm, approximately 1 percent of body height. The principal factor accounting for the change was a difference in the shape and size of the intervertebral discs, which lost fluid during the day and regained it at night. DePuky had observed that when a patient got up after being confined to bed for a time, he seemed to have grown, but that this phenomenon often failed to occur in the surgical wards because post-operative pain "will often set up some defensive rigidity in certain muscles."

The intervertebral discs are also implicated in "man's slow decline in stature." DePuky cited a study by Junghanns, who performed 1,142 post-mortem dissections of the spinal column. Junghanns found that the ratio between the thickness of the disc and the thickness of the adjacent vertebra diminished with age from 1:1 at birth to 1:2 at ten, 1:3 at twenty-four, 1:4 at sixty, and on down from there. The change was due entirely to the gradual loss of fluid from the fibrocartilage of which the discs are largely composed. According to DePuky, cartilage can absorb and release up to twenty times its volume of water. He found that discs taken from the spinal column of an aged cadaver when soaked for two days in a fixation fluid would resume the shape they had in infancy before the curves in the back had been established.

Clearly the discs are an important mechanism affecting the height as well as the comfort of the body. Like the synovial fluid in the joints, the water absorbed by the discs exerts hydraulic force on the bony structures above them. The discs are kept under pressure by ligaments and muscles. If the muscles shorten, the hydraulic force that the discs can exert is reduced; if they lengthen, it is increased. This property of the discs and of the other weight-bearing joints may explain some of the sensations reported by students of the Alexander

Technique—the sensations, for example, that parts of the body, especially the head, are buoyed up from below.

MECHANICS OF MUSCLE

Like ligaments, muscles possess elasticity and can do work by shortening. Unlike ligaments, they can increase tension without being stretched, and be stretched without increasing tension. And unlike ligaments, muscles are subject to direct voluntary control. Though muscles can work at different lengths, there is one optimal length (usually its resting length) at which in response to an adequate stimulus a muscle will exert maximal tension.

The versatility of muscle is a function of its unique structure, but it is made effective only through its connections with the central nervous system.

STRETCH REFLEXES

One stimulus to which a muscle responds by contracting is mechanical stretch. Stretch can be applied by an outside force like gravity or an inside force like the hydraulic pressure in the discs or by the contraction of other muscles. The tension generated in a muscle is proportional to the stretching force, but it can be modified (increased, decreased, or shut off altogether) by mechanisms in the nervous system that respond both to feedback from the muscle and its tendon and to signals from other parts of the organism.

The tendency of the body to lengthen from within gives it strength as well as buoyancy. If the discs have expanded (as DePuky showed), the small muscles attached to the vertebrae must have been lengthened and their strength thereby increased. (Starling showed how much the strength of contraction in heart muscle is increased by the stretch imparted to it as blood is taken into the atrium.) The lengthening and strengthening initiated by the discs and the small muscles would be transmitted by purely mechanical means to the longer muscles and the process would continue to the surface. This lengthening-strengthening process is further enhanced by movement. In moving the body or one of its parts against gravity the lift-ing muscles are facilitated by the stretch placed upon them by the part that is being lifted. (Just as in sailing a boat into the wind by tack-ing, the boat is moved forward by the force that opposes it, so a movement against gravity is facilitated by gravity itself.) In getting up from a chair, for example, the head, neck and back move forward as a unit without losing their length. In the process the muscles in the lower back, buttocks and thighs are stretched. When the stretch reaches a certain level of intensity, the stretched muscles (like the heart muscles described by Starling) contract reflexly, straightening the hip joint and in turn stretching the muscles around the knee. The body is thus lifted smoothly and easily with a sense of little or no effort. (The movement is not likely to be successful, at least for the first time, without guidance because a subject who has not had the experience of performing such a movement is apt to lose confidence at the last moment and revert back to his habitual way of moving.)

In the reflex movement described in Chapter 12 the experi-menter applied a horizontal force against the subject's back and brought him reflexly to his feet by a somewhat different use of the same mechanism. The subject's instructions for this movement are to equalize the pressure of the experimenter's hand. If he does not go forward, the resultant of the two forces will be an increase in extensor tonus sufficient to straighten the hip and knee joints, and bring him directly to his feet. Pressure should start out at zero and increase smoothly until there is just enough tonus in extensor mus-cles to overcome gravity. (Neither subject nor experimenter should do any lifting.) I was the subject for the multiple-image photograph in figure 18 (p. 129) and can remember the experience vividly. It seemed to me that I was moving up on a current of air.

Lengthening the body has an important effect upon ligaments as well as upon muscle. Ligaments can only function at their normal length. In the spinal column, for example, if muscles shorten below their resting length, the ligaments, left with nothing to do, will sag and cease to support either the vertebrae or the discs. If, on the other hand, the spine lengthens, it will regain the strengthening support of the ligaments.

HEAD–NECK REFLEXES

Sherrington once described posture as a "congeries of stretch reflexes." The word "congeries," which is defined as "aggregation" or "heap," leaves out the central unifying factor, which, as Sherrington clearly recognized, was the head relation. By themselves, stretch reflexes have no purpose or meaning. They are organized into an integrated whole by the reflexes that control the position of the head in space and its relation to the rest of the body. When an animal for any reason is out of its normal waking relation to gravity, it is brought back by the "righting reflexes," in which the head-righting reflexes play the leading rôle. If a horse, for example, has fallen, it cannot get up as long as its head is held down. Once the pressure is released, the head begins to right itself. As it does so, receptors in the joints of the neck are activated and powerful reflexes are initiated in the limbs bringing, the animal to its feet.

The principal receptors for the righting reflexes, besides the joints of the neck, are to be found in the bony labyrinths behind the ears, in the eyes and on the surface of the body. If the eyes and the labyrinths are removed, an animal will still right itself if it can feel the weight of its body pressing against a surface. If, however, the pressure of the body is equalized by a pressure exerted on the opposite side (or by placing the body in water), the animal will be completely disoriented.

The righting reflexes can operate automatically without the necessity of consciousness. Magnus described holding in his hands a rabbit surgically altered so that it could not make a voluntary movement—and feeling it right itself as if there were a piece of machinery inside.

The head–neck reflexes organize departures from the normal upright posture as well as the return to it. As the head moves, it imposes an "attitude" on the body by redistributing muscular tonus. These attitudes are imposed automatically but can be inhibited by an animal if they are not appropriate. These reflexes were extensively studied and described by Magnus and his associates. Secondary effects of attitudinal reflexes on such functions as respiration, circulation and eye position have also been demonstrated.

The immediate sensory experience of moving lightly and easily against gravity or of sensing the movement in someone else can be explained only, I believe, in reference to a central mechanism, like the righting reflexes, that integrates the anti-gravity responses. It is also the only explanation that will account for the experiences demonstrated in the first four illustrations in Chapter 12. In all of them the pattern of movement was altered and the feeling of weight was reduced as soon as the head relation was changed. To me the most convincing demonstration is the change in the walking pattern which can be made with great predictive accuracy by the lightest touch of a hand at the back of the subject's head.

Some of the structures that contribute to the efficiency of the head–neck mechanism are shown in figure 25. At the lowest level (A) are the intervertebral discs with the small muscles and ligaments that knit the vertebrae together. The hydraulic force of the discs is directed upward through the bodies of the vertebrae.

FLEXORS AND EXTENSORS OF THE NECK

The lifting force in the discs is multiplied by the tension in the extensors and flexors of the neck (B). Acting together, the two groups strengthen the cervical spine, turning it into a pillar of support for the head. In an upright posture their contractile force will be increased by the pull of gravity.

FLEXORS AND EXTENSORS OF THE HEAD, I

The muscles at the next level (C) can tilt the head forward and back, but they cannot lift it. Together with the *ligamentum nuchae* (a wide, fibrous, partially elastic band between the occiput and the 7th cervical vertebra), the extensors of the head, which have insertions at the base of the skull and various origins along the spinal column, balance the torque placed upon the head by gravity. These extensor muscles are designed to support, in addition to the weight of the head, the tension in a smaller group of flexor muscles which connect the skull with the shoulder girdle via the jaw and the hyoid bone.

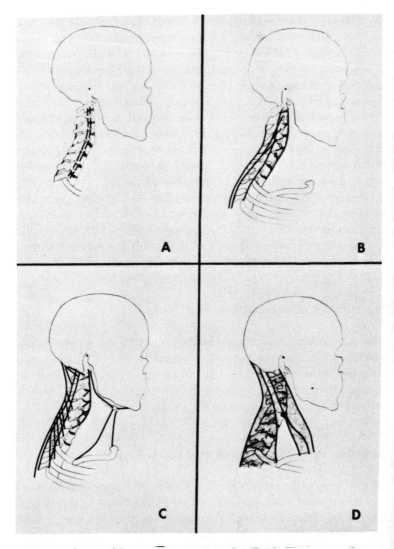

Fig. 25 Anatomical structures affecting the height and angle of the head. A. intervertebral discs with *interspinales* and *intertransversarii* muscles. B. flexors and extensors of the neck; C. flexors and extensors of the head; D. upper trapezius and sternocleidomastoid muscles.

CENTRE OF GRAVITY OF THE HEAD

In the system of forces acting on the head the centre of gravity plays a major rôle. On the surface it is conventionally located in the Frankfurt plane halfway between the tragion of the ear and the low point of the orbit. In a sagittal X-ray it is located in *sella turcica*, a landmark that is defined as the "depression in the superior surface of the body of the sphenoid bone which houses the hypophysis cerebri (pituitary gland)." Because the centre of gravity is forward from the point of support, balance must be maintained by the muscles and the ligaments attached to the occiput. This balance serves two purposes: it orients the head to the environment, and it keeps the extensor muscles under stretch from above.

The efficiency of the system is directly related to the distance between the centre of gravity and the point at which the head is balanced. Maximizing this distance (the axis of rotation) maximizes the torque on the head, stretches extensor muscles and facilitates lengthening of the spine. Conversely, shortening the distance reduces the torque and with it the stretch stimulus.

FLEXORS AND EXTENSORS OF THE HEAD, II

For the efficient operation of this system of forces sufficient space is needed so that the various muscle groups can function at their optimal length. Normally the space is provided by the mechanisms that lengthen the spine. The space may be reduced, however, by the simultaneous contraction of another group of muscles. These are two pairs of flexors and extensors, the upper trapezii and the sternocleidomastoids (D), which connect the head directly to the shoulder girdle. Acting separately, they rotate the head to the right or left, and tilt it forward and down or backward and up. Acting together, they bring the head closer to the shoulders and change the balance of forces among the other muscles of the neck. The two pairs of muscles can act very quickly (Duchenne found them the fastest of all skeletal muscles to react to electrical stimulation). Their joint action, which is supported by the other flexors and extensors of the head, can be seen most clearly in the startle pattern (figure 20, p. 131).

The startle pattern may be taken as a paradigm of malposture in general, whether it is associated with ageing, disease or lack of exercise. In malposture muscles in various combinations and degrees of tension have shortened, displacing the head or holding it in a fixed position. Head displacement would have an adverse effect on the rest of the body partly because of the added weight and the strain put upon muscles and ligaments, but largely, I believe, because of interference in the righting reflexes by abnormal pressure on the joints of the neck. What is basically an incomplete response to gravity would in time come to feel natural, and the muscles contributing to it would be strengthened by exercise.

The procedures used in the Alexander Technique establish a new dynamic balance among the forces acting on the head so as to allow more of the postural work to be done by discs and ligaments and by muscles acting at their optimal length.

As the X-rays show, the sternomastoid and upper trapezius muscles lengthen, allowing the centre of gravity of the head to move forward and the head itself to move up. "Forward and up" clearly is not a single, oblique movement but two movements, the first of which facilitates the second. Depending on where the head happens to be at the start, "forward" will bring the centre of gravity up or down. In any case, the increase in this distance increases the torque exerted by the head on extensor muscles and facilitates extension of the spine. The head feels lighter because more of its weight is carried by discs and ligaments and because muscles that move it (for example, the sternomastoids and the upper trapezii) have lengthened.

The increase in the axis of head rotation facilitates extension of the spine in all movements that we have recorded. In each of the guided movements (figures 3–6, pp. 111-13) the head moves in a greater orbit than it does in the habitual movement with which it is compared. Because the space between the vertebrae and between the first vertebra and the head increases (as the X-ray photographs show), there must be more room for blood vessels so that the flow of blood to the brain, both through the vertebral artery (which passes through the suboccipital space before entering the *foramen magnum*) and through the carotids (which hug the sternomastoid muscles as they pass through the neck) would be facilitated. It is reasonable to suppose also that the sensitivity of the pressure receptors in the carotid sinuses would be affected by changes in the length and tension of the muscles around them.

The reduction of eyestrain and the facilitation of breathing that I observed so dramatically in myself and have frequently observed in others can best be explained, I believe, as secondary effects of the head–neck reflexes. In the case of breathing, the process was further facilitated by postural changes in the lower back and the rib cage, which added stretch to the diaphragm and to the muscles of expiration. These and similar effects, when they can be observed and studied introspectively, have a higher meaning and validity than the same effects when known only from animal experimentation.

INHIBITION

None of the mechanisms that I have described can function without inhibition. Alexander's major discovery was not the "primary control" but the significance of inhibition in the intact organism.

Inhibition is a positive, not a negative force. Some degree of inhibition is essential not only for a good life but for any life at all. Inhibition maintains the integrity of the responding organism so that a particular response can be carried out economically without involving inappropriate activity in unrelated parts. (When inhibition breaks down completely, as in strychnine poisoning, any small discrete stimulus will produce convulsive shortening of muscles throughout the body.) In the presence of a stimulus to move, inhibition facilitates lengthening of the spine and adds to the efficiency of the movement. Too quick a response will shorten surface muscles in the neck and prevent the lengthening of the spine, which would otherwise take place. An example of how the mechanism works in animals was called to my attention by Majorie Barstow. In a steer-throwing contest, if the contestant grasps the horns suddenly and applies pressure immediately, the steer will be thrown to the ground by an attitudinal reflex from the neck. If, however, the contestant is too slow in acting, the steer's neck will lengthen and strengthen and the manoeuvre will fail.

Inhibition is a physiological process which does not need to be conscious in order to operate. Bringing it up to the conscious level not only establishes an indirect control over anti-gravity responses but facilitates the learning of new habits and the unlearning of those that are old and unwanted. When a stimulus is presented for the first time, many responses are available, including not making a response at all. If one of these responses is selected and learned, it can be repeated without loss of choice as long as the process remains conscious. If it drops below the level of consciousness, a "set" will be established, linking the stimulus with the response, which will then occur automatically whether it is appropriate or not. When the "set" is well established, a presentation of the stimulus will result in less tonic activity in both the sensory system (through habituation of the orienting reaction) and the motor system (through automatization). The result is a habit which operates unconsciously (like an innate reflex) and which is resistant to change. Inhibition raises the level of tonic activity in the nervous system, brings the operation of the habit to a conscious level, and restores choice (including the choice of making the original response).

The intimate connection between Alexandrian inhibition and postural tonus makes this model applicable to any learned response. For demonstration purposes getting up from a chair is the classic example. Once the thought of standing up registers, the person responds with an automatic set: neck muscles shorten and any response except the habitual (or a minor variation—a "different kind of badly") is excluded. Inhibition, by eliminating the postural set, allows a non-habitual response to be made. The spine has time to lengthen and, as movement begins, the anti-gravity reflexes are facilitated. The head is left free to modulate the response, in whatever way is conducive to a smooth movement.

If the stimulus is "mental"—a memory, a perception, an emotion—the same model applies. Delaying the response long enough to inhibit neck-muscle shortening (which may be less than a second) prevents an immediate stereotyped response from imposing itself and facilitates making a choice that is appropriate to the situation as a whole. Inhibition, to use Dewey's expression, "postpones immediate action upon desire until observation and judgement have entered in." The facilitation is physical as well as mental. It provides that whatever the response is, it will take place under optimal conditions, for example, with an adequate breathing pattern and an adequate flow of blood to the brain.

The evidence that I have assembled has been drawn from the careful observation of changes that have taken place in myself and others and a search for mechanisms that would account for them. I believe the evidence fully supports the following hypotheses:

1. The reflex response of the organism to gravity is a fundamental feedback mechanism which integrates other reflex systems.
2. Under civilized conditions this mechanism is commonly interfered with by habitual, learned responses which disturb the tonic relation between head, neck and trunk.
3. When this interference is perceived kinaesthetically, it can be inhibited. By this means the anti-gravity response is facilitated and its integrative effect on the organism is restored.

I submit that these hypotheses have face validity and are consistent with established principles of physiology and psychology.

14

Notes on Teaching

If to do were as easy as to know what were good to do, chapels had been churches, and poor man's cottages princes' palaces. It is a good divine that follows his own instructions: I can easier teach twenty what were good to be done, than be one of the twenty to follow mine own teaching.

The Merchant of Venice, I. ii

MY LAST LETTER FROM F. M. was dated September 11, 1953. He had just learned that the rent at 16 Ashley Place, where he had taught for nearly forty years and which had become a sort of shrine for overseas visitors and friends of the Technique, was to be raised a thousand pounds a year. It was a "nasty shock," he wrote. "However, I have, after considerable thought as to ways and means, decided I could not leave this place and the atmosphere that has been created in it." The lease was renewed and F. M. lived on for two more years in the atmosphere of heavy Edwardian elegance he loved. He continued to teach, and according to reports his hands lost none of their skill. He grew frailer in appearance, however, and it sometimes seemed as if it was only "the work" that kept him alive. Goddard Binkley, who was in the last training course at which F. M. officiated, remembered that he visited the class and gave everyone a "turn" a few months before he died. "He walked into the room looking, I would say, all of his eighty-six years, and I had the strong impression at the moment that if it were not for the strength and vitality of his conscious direction he would have collapsed in a heap on the floor. Certainly there was no loss of direction and effectiveness in the use of his hands. At least I did not detect any."

F. M. died on October 10, 1955, without naming a successor to carry on his teaching. Since the mantle of his authority had not fallen on any individual teacher or group of teachers, there was no one who could claim pre-eminence by right of succession. The best claimant would have been Irene Tasker, who had been in the work longer than anyone else, Ethel Webb having died shortly before F. M. Irene Tasker has continued to give private lessons but left it to others to carry on the training of teachers. Before long there were four training centres in London that were descended from and modelled after the original three-year course at Ashley Place. Training courses have also been started in the United States, and there is now a second generation of Alexander teachers, who knew neither F. M. nor A. R.

How good an example of the Technique must a teacher be? We have become used to the idea of physicians who cannot heal themselves, of child experts who ruin their own children, of singing teachers who cannot sing, and dancing teachers who cannot dance. Teaching the Alexander Technique is different. You can't teach someone else an improved use of himself until your own manner of use has improved. The Technique deals with change and development. Before he can impart what he knows to others, a teacher must have experienced in himself enough change to understand the process operationally. Furthermore, the process of change must be continuous. When a person starts teaching the Alexander Technique, he does not thereby stop learning it. On the contrary, he should be learning as much from a lesson as the pupil is. (An indignant pupil once exclaimed to me: "You are learning more from me than I am learning from you!") The teacher's primary concern must still be to increase his control over himself and his reactions. If he turns his knowledge into an instrument for establishing power over others (as he can easily do by encouraging his pupils to distrust their own thinking and their ability to learn for themselves and to become wholly dependent upon him for their progress), he is perverting the Technique.

The aim of teaching, as I conceive it, is to bring a pupil to the point of self-discovery that F.M. reached when he was able to translate what he saw in the mirrors into kinaesthetic terms and to apply his new knowledge to the solution of his own problems and become, in effect, his own expert in the use of himself. To accomplish this result I do not believe it is necessary, or desirable, or for that matter possible to follow the same steps that F. M. followed in making his discovery or that I followed when I began studying the Technique.

My aim is to give my pupil as quickly and surely as possible the benefit of my present knowledge and understanding and help him avoid the false starts and misconceptions that slowed my own progress. In discussing the Technique it is useful—in my opinion it is essential—to keep in mind the distinction between what Alexander discovered and the method he used for imparting his discovery to others. The principle of inhibition and primary control existed before Alexander discovered it by looking into a mirror. It can undoubtedly be discovered again, not necessarily by the same route. As Aldous Huxley said: "One has to make the discovery oneself, starting from scratch." If a pupil doesn't make it, his lessons as lessons are wasted, no matter how much he may benefit from them therapeutically.

Thirty years ago when I first began teaching, what impressed me most, next to the importance of the principle that Alexander discovered, was the difficulty of conveying a sense of that importance to someone else. I am more impressed than ever by the importance of the principle, but I am also impressed by its simplicity and the ease with which it can be demonstrated.

What makes a good pupil? It is not suggestibility. The person who sits down, relaxes and prepares to have some kind of novel experience may get what he is looking for, but it will not be the Alexander Technique. A healthy scepticism is much easier to deal with.

If there were a reliable test for "use," which could be administered routinely without making the pupil self-conscious, it might be worthwhile to obtain objective records from time to time as a measure of progress. I am opposed, however, to tests of specific functions, unless they are used as part of a research programme. Test results are difficult to interpret; they set the wrong tone by stressing specific ends rather than means. The same thing is true of diagnosis. It produces a medical atmosphere and in the pupil's mind suggests the idea of cure. From the point of view of teaching there is nothing to be gained and something to be lost in telling a prospective pupil that he has a dropped shoulder, a hump on his back, a spinal curvature, a weak voice or a timid manner. Diagnosis makes a pupil self-conscious about specific faults. If he does not perceive them kinaesthetically, the information will not mean anything to him and may slow down learning by adding to anxiety. (In one of Alexander's early works he makes the statement that "there is no disrobing." It might

be well to repeat the statement here, since a recent book suggests
that the Technique involves a complete physical examination. As the
Alexanders taught it and as most people teach it today, it definitely
does not.)

I try to find out first what the pupil's interests are and relate them
to the Technique. I explain what I mean by kinaesthetic perception
—that it deals with the sensations of position and movement, of heaviness and lightness, of tension, effort and fatigue—and add that the
purpose of the Technique is to organize this information, which
comes from within the self, so that it can be perceived in relation to
the information that is coming from outside. I then call attention to
the rôle of the head in postural responses, sometimes illustrating my
explanation with examples taken from animal movement and usually giving a brief account of F. M.'s experiments with the mirrors.
After this I say that F. M.'s second discovery, more important in a way
than his first, was that by using his hands he could communicate
information directly through the kinaesthetic sense (which I have
just defined). I then proceed to the demonstration, asking the pupil
to stay where he is while I make him aware kinaesthetically of where
his head is in space—that is, in relation to the environment—and
where it is in relation to the rest of the body, explaining that this is
a dynamic and not a static relation, since the head always has the
potential for movement. I start out in this way (without any other pre-
liminaries) in order to emphasize the fact that the Technique can
be applied wherever a person is and whatever he happens to be
doing. I do not ask a pupil to lie down on a table or sit in a special
chair before I begin teaching; I do not place him in a "position of
mechanical advantage," or do anything else to suggest that the Technique is concerned with special "Alexander positions" or exercises.

When I touch the pupil's head with my hand, I explain that I do
not want him to change his head position by making a voluntary
movement, but that there are two reflex responses that his head can
make to the pressure of my hand. One is a shortening response (like
the response that is seen in the startle pattern) in which the muscles
at the nape of the neck shorten, bringing the head closer down in
the direction of the shoulders. The other response is in the opposite direction: the muscles lengthen and the head moves farther out.
I ask the pupil to allow the second of these two responses to take place

and in this way to inhibit the first. Starting with a minimal pressure around the occiput and mastoid process, I gradually increase it as I sense a lengthening of the neck. While I am eliciting this response I expand the pupil's field of attention by asking him to notice (without giving up the awareness of his head) something else at the same time—the pressure of my other hand against his back, the pressure of the floor against his feet, the image of something in his visual field. I then ask him to carry out some movement—to get up if he is sitting down, or take a step or two if he is standing—while I keep my hand at his head to call attention to the relation that has been established. He may get off to a jerky start. I do not ask him to repeat it but to let me initiate the next movement for him and to notice the difference between the two movements. Very soon the facilitated movements will begin to feel easier than the habitual. The pupil will feel that he is lighter, that he is occupying more space and using less effort than before. I do not keep my hand at his head very long at a time—just long enough to make an impression, which I can renew from time to time. The teacher's hands are like a catalytic agent in a chemical experiment. They release a process that goes on without them. The lengthening response of the head and neck can be made to any external stimulus. The stimulus of gravity is always there and the body can lengthen to it as well as shorten, once it has learned, or rather relearned, how to make the response.

Ultimately a pupil must be able to make reliable kinaesthetic observations of himself in activity. Such observations, however, cannot be performed by the suggestions of the teacher. The purpose of lessons is to sharpen the kinaesthetic sense and to increase self-knowledge and self-control. The purpose is not to help the pupil develop his fantasy life. To imagine, for example, that your head is a balloon (which it certainly is not) is to get further away from reality than you already are and to reduce your chances of ever observing the head relation for what it is and does. Movement within an expanded field of attention is the means by which change is effected in the Alexander Technique. It cannot be effected by substituting imagination for attention.

The model of moving within an expanded field of attention can be applied to any activity. In addition to sitting down, standing up, and walking, I use stair climbing, working at a desk, reading aloud, handling small objects, moving furniture or anything else that seems appropriate. I have demonstrated the Technique to dancers doing pliés, to musicians playing their instruments, to T'ai Chi students practising the movements they have learned. While they are giving the major part of their attention to what they are doing—the "end" they are gaining—I ask them to expand their field of attention enough to take in the facilitation of the postural response that I am providing.

Psychologists have collected a great deal of experimental evidence to show that perceptual learning is very much more effective if the subject is allowed to make some voluntary use of his muscles during the learning process. In animal studies the term "reafference" has been used to describe the neural excitation that follows sensory stimulation produced by voluntary movements of the animal doing the sensing.

The principle of reafference applies in teaching the Alexander Technique whenever the pupil is encouraged to move voluntarily while the teacher facilitates some aspect of the anti-gravity response. This joint procedure provides a unique learning experience. Instead of depending passively on a teacher for whatever new experiences he obtains, the pupil becomes an active participant in the operation, taking major responsibility for what happens. With the teacher's help he has an opportunity to monitor his own performance and thus to develop a technique of his own for integrating thought with action.

I like this way of presenting the Technique better than the way in which it was presented to me. My pupils learn to use conscious direction and inhibition without verbalizing it. After they have acquired sufficient confidence in their own thinking and are able to give attention to what they are doing without end-gaining, they can use words "for keeping close track of what is going on," as John Dewey put it, "words as names certainly being the great clinchers in an operation." I found directions (directing my neck to relax, my head to go forward and up, etc.) useful at a certain stage in learning the Technique, especially when my mind wandered and I floated off in a stream of associations, or when I was distracted by some pain or discomfort and had difficulty giving my full attention to the Technique. Soon, however, they took on a ritualistic quality and began to lose their effectiveness. I found that I was verbally giving directions but nothing was happening. A. R. made me realize that directions alone were not the equivalent of thinking in activity but that something beyond words was needed.

There are two difficulties inherent in the use of words for learning the Alexander Technique. First, they can get in the way of observing and act as a substitute for thought. Feedback is an essential part of the Technique. If you are not allowing your spine to lengthen while you are making some response, there will be a decrease of freedom in your movements. In that case it is important to be aware of what is happening so that you can re-establish your control, but if you are saying directions to yourself you may miss what is happening because the directions have become an end in themselves. Second, words carry connotations with them from earlier experiences. Such words as "relax," "forward and up," "lengthen and widen," already have meanings that may get in the way and prevent you from having new experiences. In talking about the Technique to a pupil I try to use different words from time to time so that he will get away from the notion that there is a one-to-one relation between the word and the thing.

Two words that have to be used with caution are "feeling" and "thinking." They are often contrasted with each other (wrongly, in my opinion) as if they were mutually exclusive and as if one of them was good and the other bad. Instead of "feeling," which is vague, subjective and imprecise, I prefer "observing," "noticing" or "being aware." You can notice or be aware of how you are reacting to a situation, and the report that you make of your observations can be independently checked by another observer. Your feelings, on the other hand, are accessible only to you.

Whenever possible I like to use "knowing," "perceiving" or "consciously allowing" instead of "thinking." It is difficult to think without using words or symbols, but knowing, perceiving and allowing are essentially non-verbal. "Thinking" usually means "thinking about;" sometimes it means "imagining," which can get you quickly off the track. As F. M. himself found out, you can think that you are putting your head "forward and up" when you are actually pulling it "backward and down." What you want is to be able to *know* when you are pulling your head down and when you are allowing it to go up. The Alexander Technique might be defined as a method for knowing simultaneously what you are not doing as well as what you are doing—knowing, for example, that you are not interfering with the "primary control" while you are talking, listening or thinking, using the term in the sense of "problem solving" or "ratiocinating." ("Verbal orders" would be bound to interfere with all three of these activities.)

"Perception" has been defined as the process of knowing objects and events by means of the senses. Traditionally it has been divided up according to sense modalities—visual perception, auditory perception, tactile perception, and so on. More recently a tendency has grown for treating the field as a unity in which divisions according to particular senses are arbitrary. One division that is still regularly made is the division between the environment and the self, the term "perception" being limited to the former and "proprioception" used for the latter only. Perception, it is sometimes asserted, can be directed only one way at a time—either out or in. The practice of the Alexander Technique, however, creates an expanded field of attention in which the interaction of the self and the environment is perceived as an ongoing process. The perceptual field has a very simple organization, but it always takes in both the self (including the relation of the head to the trunk) and something of the environment. Thus the teacher perceives what he himself is doing as well as what the pupil is doing.

Any teaching device is legitimate if it speeds learning and does not become an end in itself. One of the most effective devices that I have found for heightened awareness is the strain-gauge force platform described in Chapter 12. Displaying the preliminary shift in weight as a person gets ready to move can give him a valuable insight into the problem of set. It becomes easier to demonstrate the meaning of inhibition and the importance of head balance when he can see that what he is doing is causing the pen on the physiograph to deflect. Videotape can also be helpful both to the teacher and to the pupil if it is used in the right way. On four occasions I have recorded the first and last sessions of a class. It made a great impression on all who participated and gave them a new understanding of the process when they could observe the changes that had taken place in themselves. I did not let them look at the first tape, however, until the second one was available for comparison.

The paradigm of learning which up to now has applied to all of my exposition of the Alexander Technique has been that of a trans-action in which new sensory experiences are imparted by a teacher to a pupil in order to help him in changing his habitual manner of responding to stimuli. It should not be forgotten, however, that Alexander himself did not have the help of a teacher, and there is no reason why someone else should not make the same discovery. "Anyone," said F. M., "can do what I do if he does what I did." In practice, few seem to have succeeded in accomplishing this. The reason, I am sure, is that in spite of warnings they "turn it into a doing." People have frequently introduced themselves to me with the statement: "I have read Mr. Alexander's books and I always try to hold my head in the right position, which he advocates." This, of course, is just what he did not advocate. He discovered an inhibitory control which has nothing to do with position. This was not an idle chance discovery. It followed a series of careful observations of the way he responded to the stress of public recitation. If you wanted to establish a similar control without expert assistance, you could design a few simple experiments in which you could subject yourself to mild stress and observe its effect on the muscles of your neck. For instance, if you lie down on your back and anticipate the effort you would make in order to sit up, you may detect an increase in tension in your neck even before you begin to move. See if you can inhibit this increase as you continue to think of sitting up but don't sit up. Then decide not to sit up but bring your right knee up while you inhibit the increase in neck-muscle tension. (Note that you are not relaxing tension that is already there but inhibiting an increase in response to the thought of raising your knee.) You may judge your success in two ways: 1) by how well you sustain your resolution to inhibit and 2) by the movement of the knee, which should follow a different pathway from the one it would ordinarily follow.

Another experimental situation you might devise would be to expose yourself to a disagreeable sound like an alarm clock or a piece of squeaking chalk, or merely to think of such a sound, and to observe in as much detail as possible how your body responded, giving special attention to the response of your head and neck. After obtaining a fairly clear perception of the pattern of your response, you could then experiment by inhibiting the change in level of neck-muscle tension and observing any changes that might take place in the rest of the response pattern.

These or similar procedures would be very much more successful if you had the help of a competent teacher to give you a direct experience of inhibition and to assist you in your experiments until you could proceed with confidence by yourself. But since the Alexander Technique is nothing more than the application of experimental method to problems of everyday behaviour, there is no reason to delay the undertaking if a teacher is not available.

I used to wish that there was something I could carry with me at all times to tell me whether I was or was not pulling my head down, something like the "ring of conscience" in the fairy tale that would prick my finger or ring a bell whenever I stopped thinking about my head and neck. Biofeedback had not been invented at that time, but I doubt now that it would have helped much. The principle behind biofeedback is different from the principle behind the Alexander Technique. Biofeedback is concerned with extending control of the mind over particular bodily systems, especially the autonomic nervous system. Signals from the body are fed back in the form of visual or auditory displays and used consciously to reduce blood pressure, slow the heart or increase the amount of alpha rhythm in the electroencephalogram. From the Alexander point of view biofeedback is an undesirable and possibly dangerous interference in the homeostatic balance of the organism. Who knows at any particular time how high (or how low) his blood pressure should be, or how fast his heart should be beating? Alexander believed that these questions should be turned over to the wisdom of the body instead of burdening the individual with every decision. A better case might be made for the electrical activity of skeletal muscle, especially neck muscle, but even here biofeedback begs all the important questions from the Alexander point of view. The Alexander Technique is not concerned with relaxation as such. It is concerned with the overall relation of muscle length to muscle tension, but I know of no mechanical device by which this relation can be recorded. If there were some kind of portable signal, I fear that the pupil would soon cease to heed it or would find it so irritating that, like the prince in the fairy tale who threw away the ring of conscience, he would shut it off. Only so much of the Technique can be absorbed at one time and only the pupil can determine how much that will be.

A. R. Alexander used to say that faith is necessary in the Alexander Technique as well as in religion, but that in the Alexander Technique if you really have faith you will be immediately rewarded. "Immediate reinforcement" is a concept that is familiar to psychologists who recognize the importance of having the reward follow immediately after a response that is to be learned. In the Alexander Technique when a student is inhibiting his habitual response and allowing his spine to lengthen and his head to move in the direction of greater freedom, any movement that he makes will register kinaesthetically as pleasanter, more efficient and more desirable than his habitual movement. In other words, he is immediately rewarded. Later on when he returns to his old way of sitting or standing, this will feel uncomfortable in contrast with his new set of experiences. By this means the reinforcement is clearly associated with the response that is being learned. I consider it important in teaching the Technique that the facilitated response should be its own reward. Praise or blame from the teacher (in my opinion) slows down learning, by bringing in an extraneous factor. The pupil is apt to attribute praise to something he did rather than what he did not do, so that the wrong aspect of the response is being reinforced. In the Alexander Technique, one is teaching a new way of responding to stimuli, and it is essential, if the response is to become established, that it have an intrinsic reward that is built into the response itself. I know of no other educational or therapeutic system that offers an immediate, sensory reward for not doing some action that has become habitual. In the past a great variety of rewards and punishments have been devised in the attempt to change habitual learned responses. A new approach is available and it is long overdue.

Francis Bacon was the first to stress the importance of the negative instance in scientific reasoning. Negative instances are important both for testing and for defining the boundaries of a generalization. In accounts of the Alexander Technique negative instances are conspicuously absent. The anecdotes and case histories used for illustrative purposes by F. M. and others all have happy endings. F. M. himself seemed to be reluctant to admit that there was anyone to whom the Technique could not be taught. In theory perhaps he was right. Though I believe that one essential condition for successful teaching is the ability of the pupil to sustain attention for some definable minimum of time, I do not believe that anyone would be prevented by his physical condition or state of health from learning the Technique. In practice, however, there are plenty of negative instances. It would be more scientific, the critics say, and might throw light on the principles underlying the Technique, to collect and examine the negative instances—the failures as well as the successes.

There have always been failures of pupils to learn the Alexander Technique, not counting those who refuse to try it in the first place. Some of the failures may have been due to bad teaching—to the teacher's ineptness with words, or his inability to convey the kinaesthetic experience in a meaningful way, or his refusal to adapt his way of teaching to the pupil's needs. Though good teaching certainly speeds up the process of learning, anyone within the limitations set forth above can learn the Technique if he is determined to do so.

Pupils give many reasons for discontinuing lessons or for not going on with the study by themselves: they are too old to learn; they aren't intellectual enough; they don't have the time or the money. These are excuses, not reasons. I believe that the real reason some pupils do not go on is a fear of self-knowledge and a deep-seated reluctance to change. People who start lessons because they are hoping to find something or someone outside themselves to solve their problems are often shocked to discover that the solution lies within themselves.

When you know "sensorily" that what you are doing is harmful to yourself and others, you can continue doing it but you are making a deliberate choice and cannot plead ignorance. You can no longer explain your behaviour exclusively in terms of nature and nurture—in terms of your genetic heritage and your previous experiences. A third factor, how you are using yourself in activity, must be considered. Unlike the other two, this factor can be brought under conscious control.

The Alexander Technique sets a person free from the slavery of habit, but it brings responsibility with it. I believe the reason some pupils stop having lessons in spite of obvious benefits they are receiving is the realization that if they go on further they will have to take increasing responsibility for their acts. The Technique is not a treatment; it is a discipline that, to be effective, has to be applied in the activities of daily life. The reward is an increase in competence and self-esteem and in the sensory satisfaction that accompanies self-knowledge and self-control.

Appendix A

F. M. Alexander and the Re-education of Feeling

John Dewey once said that the reason F. M. Alexander's teaching had appealed to him in the first place was not that it made him feel better (though the improvement in his health had been marked), but that it made him conscious of his total ignorance of a whole field of knowledge. The field he referred to was the knowledge of how he used himself in the ordinary activities of life. Like many intellectuals Dewey was aware of a certain ineptness in the performance of physical tasks. If he was going to get up from a chair, or sit down, or pick up something he had dropped, he would do it awkwardly, and his aim was to get it over with as quickly as possible so as to get on to something more suited to his abilities, like "thinking." Alexander made him realize that his impressions and beliefs about his own physical activities were as appropriate a field as any for the exercise of constructive thought.

Kinaesthetic impressions—the sensations of position, mass and movement of the organism and its parts—bulk very large in the sum of the impressions received by the brain. In point of conscious organization, however, these impressions and the beliefs we have formed about them have not passed much beyond the stage of what William James called "buzzing confusion." In comparison with our knowledge of the forces operating in the external world we know next to nothing about the forces operating inside our own skins. We are often aware, to be sure, of certain feelings of awkwardness, effort, pain, fatigue and the like. If these feelings are mild or temporary we generally ignore them. If they persist or become severe we may consult an expert of one kind or another. The expert, however, in making a diagnosis, is apt to discount the report of our feelings in favour of "objective evidence." In this, of course, he is right, since our feelings cannot have any real significance for another person. If it is important that this kind of data should be organized and given meaning the individual has to do it for himself. The peculiar merit of F. M. Alexander, in my opinion, is that he discovered a practical means by which the individual can do just this—organize his feelings and beliefs about himself into a coherent system. The result, as has always been the case when a body of facts has been organized systematically, is not only an increase of knowledge, but a release of energy and an extension of control.

About fifty years ago, Alexander, then an elocutionist and public speaker whose voice had begun to fail him during speaking engagements, made a series of acute self-observations in the course of which he was able to correlate changes in the poise of his head as seen in a mirror with changes in the quality of his voice. He discovered that loss of voice was regularly preceded by a perceptible alteration of the tensional balance of his head in relation to his neck, and of his head and neck in relation to the rest of his body. By patient experiment he devised a means for preventing the initial change in the head–neck relation and thus indirectly preventing the loss of voice. When he was able to put the new control to use he found that the beneficial effect did not stop with his voice but extended in some degree to all his activities.

At this point I should like to emphasize the significance of the head–neck relationship. When Alexander looked in the mirror he saw a change taking place in the relation of his head to his body; and he *proved* to his own satisfaction that in himself this change was responsible for other changes of an adverse nature. I do not think there is any doubt that what he observed was an interference in the head–neck reflexes. Since the experimental work of Rudolph Magnus and his associates these reflexes have been generally recognized by physiologists to be of primary importance in animal movement. Alexander's observations, though he put them to good practical use, were largely empirical, and a scientific investigation of the rôle of the head–neck reflexes in human behaviour remains yet to be made.

From his experiences Alexander developed a method of teaching which he called the F. M. Alexander Technique. Its aim is to enable a student to establish in himself the kind of conscious control that Alexander had established. The Technique consists in part of a carefully worked-out set of verbal directions for the student to follow in order to inhibit his habitual response and substitute for it a new use of himself in activity. In the course of his teaching, however, Alexander discovered that he could give a student directly the immediate, kinaesthetic experience of the new use of himself if he made certain preliminary changes in the tensional balance (not, necessarily, in the position) of the student's head, neck and back, and then initiated a movement, or persuaded the student himself to move, without altering the relationship of the head to the body. The redistribution of tension that follows such a movement can frequently be grasped without explanation, as a fact of experience. From one point of view, this part of the Technique is more important than the other, since any form of strictly verbal communication is imperfect at best. When, however, teacher and student have certain shared experience, words can be used, not to describe the unknown, but to clarify "thinking" and help build up an operational formulation about something that is already known.

Aldous Huxley and others who have studied with Alexander begged off from describing their kinaesthetic experiences on the ground that it would be like trying to describe colour to someone who had been blind from birth. The experience, however, is, in a sense, the crux of the system; and I believe that an attempt should be made to describe it in spite of the poverty of our kinaesthetic vocabulary. The best procedure seems to me to use the first person and confine my account to what I myself have observed, both in lessons given me by F. M. Alexander and his brother, the late A. R. Alexander, and subsequently in my own teaching. In this way I can vouch for my own statements. I don't wish to give the impression, however, that I am describing something that is private or mystical. What I have to say can be checked against the observations of others who have studied the method.

The first and most important requisite is that of awareness. Without it I do not know how the necessary control could be established. Few people, of course, are so wrapped up in what they are doing or what they are thinking as to be completely unaware of themselves. In the course of twenty-four hours the physical self is apt to make itself felt in one way or another by even the busiest of "thinkers." But most people resent this kind of intrusion upon their "higher thoughts" and react immediately to get rid of the sensation by doing something about it. If a man who has been standing a long time becomes uncomfortable, he usually shifts his weight and forgets about it until he becomes uncomfortable somewhere else. From the practical point of view he has accomplished what he wants. But from the point of view of finding out what caused the discomfort in the first place he has accomplished nothing. To establish a control based on knowledge it is essential to take in a situation as fully as possible before making a change.

Awareness in itself, however, is not enough. Before my meeting with the Alexander brothers I had considerable awareness of myself, not only of my thoughts but of my physical sensations—or so it seemed to me. But these sensations had no meaning. They were vague and undifferentiated and gave no indication of the relations that inhered in them. In this lack I realize that I was not alone. William James pointed out that the "palpitating inward life," of which he was himself a keen observer, is "by most men over-looked." Even Sir Charles Sherrington, who knows as much as anyone about how the human nervous and muscular system works, once said that when it came to a particular activity such as standing, his mind told him next to nothing and he was unable "to think (himself) into the 'how' of the body's doing."

Like Sherrington I didn't know any more about my standing than "that it was I who stood," though the sensation differed from time to time, depending on how tired I was. When I attempted to analyse it, I concentrated my attention upon whatever part was outstanding. But in doing so I lost sight of what was going on elsewhere, and any knowledge I picked up had no real meaning or value because it was unrelated to anything else.

At the time of which I speak it did not occur to me that the problem could be solved, or, indeed, that there was a problem. I realized it only after A. R. Alexander had shown me that it is possible and, in fact, a good deal easier, once you are aware of a sensation, instead of concentrating upon one part or feature of it, to let your attention expand until it takes in certain key relationships within the organism, so that the particular part or feature of the sensation has a

meaning in relation to the whole. This "extended field of consciousness," as I have called it, is to me the essential formulation for organizing kinaesthetic impressions into an intelligible system, and I
should like to go into it a little more fully.

The "concept" is built around the sensed relationship of the head
to the rest of the body. The attention, once it has been focused upon
the head, is not shifted to another part, but extended by a process
of what may be called "unconcentrating" until it takes in the body as
well. Because the body, no matter how badly it is working, is still a
unity, consciousness can be extended throughout the field without
effort. The procedure, in fact, is subtractive of effort rather than
additive, the sense of effort being used as a criterion to judge whether
you are off the track.

It may not be possible at first to maintain the conscious field for
very long or to push it very far. But as long as there is any extension
in time-space from the head as a centre, tensional relationships can
be perceived that would otherwise be incapable of discrimination.
The process is analogous to the extension that takes place in the
visual field when a telescope is turned upon an object, so that relationships immediately stand out that were previously unperceived.

The fluctuating tensions I began to perceive in various parts of
my body were not, I discovered, a chaos, as I had supposed. They were
interrelated in a recognizable pattern. In it the dominant relationship seemed to be among the tensions of the neck and back, corresponding to what the biologist, George E. Coghill, called the "total
pattern." Tensions in other parts, the arms, legs or jaw, for example,
seemed to be subordinate to it. In response to a stimulus there was
a wave-like change of tensional level starting in the neck and following the line of the spinal column. This change was followed almost
instantly by changes elsewhere. The sequence seemed so right and
natural that the possibility of altering it, even as an experiment, did
not enter my head. The experiment, however, was performed for me,
and I was convincingly shown that it is possible to receive a stimulus
consciously and not respond to it by changing tensional levels in the
neck and back. I was also shown that if I refused to make the habitual
response, the whole pattern was different, and the movement that
followed had a kinaesthetic character unlike anything in my previous experience.

As my awareness was heightened I kept noticing the same wave-like change of tension appear as part of my response to a great variety of stimuli. If I started to sit down in a chair, if someone asked me a sudden question, if the telephone rang, the same pattern appeared. Gradually it became clear to me that here was a mechanism through which habits could not only be more clearly understood but more effectively controlled and changed—not this habit and that habit, but habits in general.

Habit and change, however, are not the aspects of Alexander's discovery I want to discuss now. What I started out to talk about was the possibility of increasing organized knowledge. The subject can be treated from two approaches, the manner of the "knowing" and the nature of the "known." I have already said something about both, but I should like to add some further remarks.

Experiential knowledge is often divided into two kinds according to whether it is obtained from within the self by "introspection" or from without by what C. Judson Herrick has called "extraspection." This is, certainly, a convenient way of dividing "knowledge." There is always a gain, however, if a dichotomy can be resolved, and it seems to me that Alexander's discovery makes it feasible to resolve this one. The terms *extraspection* and *introspection* suggest that you can only look one way at a time, either outward or inward. In what I have called an "extended field of consciousness," however, there is no such either-or situation. The centre or core of the field is the head–neck–back relationship. Around it can be integrated the sensory impressions not only of the body but of the environment as well. Within the field you can be conscious at once of the hand and the object it is holding, of the eye and what it sees; and a scientist bent over a test tube can, without loss of precision, take in within the same field of consciousness the sensations originating in his own neck and back as well as in the preparation he is observing. The fact that some of the data are visual and some kinaesthetic is of no real significance, since each sense datum, no matter what its origin, has its own place within a pattern that can at any time be integrated by an act of attention. Such an act, to coin another term like Herrick's, might be called "perspection." The observer is stationed where, instead of looking out upon his environment or in upon himself, he is looking *through* in such a way that the continuity between organism and environment appears unbroken. This does not mean that every detail on both sides of the line must be taken in. The attention is focused wherever it is wanted. But it is focused in such a way that when something in the environment is central, consciousness of the organism is not lost; and when the centre is within the organism, consciousness of the environment remains.

So much for the manner of "knowing." What are "known" are the changing tensional relationships within the self, using the term self in its broadest sense. What first strikes anyone who makes even a superficial study of the Technique is the universality of what psychologists call "set." I believe that I can make the meaning clear by using the hackneyed example of reaching for a lead pencil and again drawing upon my experience. I found that when the image of the pencil registered as an "object to be reached for," a series of tensional changes took place, starting as usual with the change in the head, neck and back and culminating in a characteristic pattern that we oriented or pointed in the direction of my pencil. When my hand and arm began to move, the increase of tension was accelerated until the pencil was reached. Once the overt movement was under way it was hard to control, for the character of the pattern and the rate of acceleration were determined by what happened before the start— by the preliminary set. Alexander discovered a means by which set can be recognized and avoided. I have already described something of the process by which this is done. In the instance of the lead pencil I was able experimentally to avoid the preliminary change in the head–neck relationship and still reach for the pencil. When I did so the hand and arm moved without any sensible increase of tension. That is, the tension that had previously characterized the movement vanished and it became kinaesthetically a different thing. The experience of moving without preliminary set is sometimes startling. Like a character in one of Einstein's hypothetical glass-walled rooms, you find that the laws governing movement are different for you than they appear to an outside observer. By obvious signs you know that you are moving your hand, but the familiar tensional hallmarks of the movement are absent.

Because the experience I have just described can be repeated at any time and under the most varied circumstances, the student has a kinaesthetic standard with which he can construct norms for his own reaction behaviour. The sense of balance in the head–neck–back relation serves as a background or screen against which a particular reaction-pattern may be judged. If the stimulus is received without disturbing this balance, you may know that you are making a controlled, ordered and "normal" response. On the other hand, the response ceases to be "normal" whenever the balance is thrown off. (I am using the term *normal* to mean what is best and most efficient for the individual at the time. I am not referring to a statistical average.)

The obvious application of a kinaesthetic standard is in problems that are commonly classed as physical, like the improvement of posture or the reduction of fatigue. There is so far as I know, however, a kinaesthetic element in all behaviour, and the standard, once it has been established, can be used with equal profit to throw light on problems that are thought of as predominantly "mental." Take, for example, verbal communication. It frequently happens that words, instead of conveying directly the meaning that was intended, act as stimuli to set off a train of thought whose character is determined more by past experiences than by the actual context. There are few who read or listen who are not in some degree the slaves of this kind of "free association." To be swept off occasionally on a side stream of thought may be only a harmless distraction; but it can, on the other hand, lead to one of those "irrational" reactions of fear, anger, disgust or the like, that serve so often to hamper communication. Now, such a response involves marked kinaesthetic components and will identify itself in a trained subject by its disruptive effect on the reflex pattern. Anyone who is interested can by this means classify stimulus-words according to the amount of reflex disturbance they create within himself.

The increase of kinaesthetic discrimination for its own sake would be of limited appeal. To know that the way you are standing makes you tired, that you overreact to verbal stimuli, that your attention has a tendency to wander, is not of itself of much practical value. Fortunately, what Alexander discovered was a means for making changes as well as recognizing the need for them. This is not, of course, a matter of sudden revelation and dramatic conversion. It implies a continual process of self-education. In the process, however, the extension of knowledge and the extension of control are conterminous. It was his experience of this kind of ordered change that led John Dewey to describe Alexander's discovery as a "new scientific principle with respect to the control of human behaviour as important as any principle that has ever been discovered in the domain of external nature."

Appendix B

The Organization of Awareness

STUDIES OF AWARENESS and of such related topics as consciousness and attention have recently begun to appear with increasing frequency in the psychological literature. For a long period of time-roughly from the 1920s to the 1950s—such concepts were rejected by psychologists as too vague, subjective and mentalistic for scientific study. I have never understood the logic of this position. To me the great appeal of psychology as a science has always been the prospect of achieving a more rational control of human behaviour—I do not mean other people's behaviour (which is the way the term is generally used); I mean one's own. But if "control" is expanded to include "self-control" you have to have a concept of awareness. So I am glad the term is becoming scientifically respectable again.

To start out with a tentative definition—awareness is knowledge of what is going on while it is happening—of what you are doing while you are doing it. It is a generalized alertness to present events. It must be admitted, however, that awareness of what you are doing is not everybody's primary goal. Many people on the contrary prefer to be *unaware* of what they are doing. They aim at a kind of learning that will give them automatically the right response for any situation. The advantage of learning something so well that you can do it automatically is, they say, that you can think of something else while you are doing it—something that is more interesting or more important. I have a colleague who always drives the ten miles to school by exactly the same route at exactly the same time in the morning. With his mind thus freed from making decisions he can plan his lectures for

A paper read at a conference on "Co-ordination in Music" at Michigan State University, May 18, 1967.

the day. Some musicians have told me that they do better when they do not have to think about what they are playing. An old Bostonian who had been a concert pianist when she was young but gave up her career after her marriage was asked to play at a small dinner party given by Koussevitsky. Searching for something Koussevitsky did not know she chose a piece which she had not played since the turn of the century. All she remembered was the opening chords, but by abstracting herself and looking steadily at a picture of a mountain lake which hung behind the piano she was able to finish the piece without a flaw and with the warm applause of the host. Had she thought for a minute of what she was doing, she said, the feat would have been impossible.

Countless examples could, I am sure, be cited of this ability to carry out smoothly a skilled and well-learned performance while following a totally different train of thought. It is not always an advantage, however. Stories about absent-minded professors are legion. In most of them the professor appears as a lovable eccentric who does something inappropriate or ridiculous while his mind is on higher things. Such episodes are less funny if they happen to you. Once you are in the habit of thinking of other things than what you are doing it may become hard to stop. And there is no guarantee that these other things will be "higher." Another musician with the ability to play automatically was not so successful as the old Bostonian in keeping his mind on peaceful scenes. Halfway through a concert performance he started thinking about a quarrel he had had that morning with his wife. This train of thought became so absorbing that by the end of the second movement in the piece he was playing, his attention was engrossed completely. He was unable to start the third movement and had to leave the stage with the piece unfinished.

In my view the chief disadvantage of automatic performance is that without awareness it cannot be changed. Socrates when asked whether it was better to do wrong knowingly or unknowingly shocked his listeners by replying that it was better to do it knowingly. If you know that it is wrong, he explained, you can change. Otherwise you cannot.

Even if a habit is good, it loses something if it becomes unconscious and stereotyped. People grow older, circumstances change, fashions change and a manner of responding or a style of perform-

ance may cease to be appropriate. It is not enough for someone else
to point this out, however. You have to know yourself what you are
doing in order to change it.

I should like to discuss a method for organizing awareness in
such a way that a performance can be well-learned without becoming stereotyped and mindless, and hence incapable of change. The
key is to be found in the relation between awareness and another
conscious state, attention. Awareness, as I conceive it, is a general
unfocused condition in which a person is wide awake and alert to
whatever may be going on without being concentrated on anything
in particular. Attention, on the other hand, is focused on some particular aspect of the field. It has been compared to a spotlight on a
dark stage. William James defines it as "the taking possession by the
mind" of one out of several possible objects or trains of thought.[1]
(Physiologists say that attention can be distinguished from inatten-
tion by measurable differences in brain waves, heart rate and other
indices.) The ability to give attention—to concentrate—is much
sought after and is often valued in proportion to its intensity and the
degree to which everything else is shut out. The often cited examples
of Archimedes drawing circles in the sand, unaware that the city of
Syracuse had been captured; and of Scaliger intent upon his commentary on Homer while the Massacre of St. Bartholomew took place
outside his window, are extreme cases, to be sure, but they illustrate
the common notion of concentration as a narrowing of the field of
attention. They also illustrated the danger in concentration—the
danger that something important is happening *outside* the field of
attention without ever being observed. The spotlight may be too
bright and the rest of the field too dark to make the observation. In
the method which I am going to describe, attention instead of being
narrowed is expanded to take in certain key relations in the body as
well as the activity on which attention is focused. To use the figure
of the spotlight and stage again, this time the spot is still bright but
the stage is merely dim instead of blacked out.

The organism has at various times been divided and subdivided
into a great many parts and categories—the mind and the body, the
five senses, the vascular system and the like. Though for purposes of
study these categories are convenient and perhaps necessary, there
is always a danger of thinking that the divisions are real, and it is

customary nowadays to start any treatise on human behaviour by affirming the unity of the organism. There is one division, however, that is seldom questioned—the division between the self and the environment. It is regularly assumed that attention must be directed either outward into the environment or inward into the self. Gibson in a new and stimulating book on *The Senses Considered as Perceptual Systems* rejects completely the traditional classification of sense data. He keeps, however, the dichotomy of "outward" and "inward," using the term "perception" for one and "proprioception" for the other.[2] "Perception," he says, "has to do with the environment. Proprioception with the body."

I should like to take a strictly unitarian approach to the problem and deny the necessity for making any such division, even for convenience. Information about the state of the body and the state of the environment is being recorded in the brain at one and the same time. Attention is ordinarily directed either one way or the other but there is no reason why this need always be the case, since the organism is capable of selecting the stimuli to which it will respond.

A scientist in a laboratory bent over a microscope tends to give his attention exclusively to the specimen he is examining. If in the course of time he becomes aware of pain or discomfort in his neck and back he either ignores it or stops what he is doing in order to give it his attention. It is perfectly possible, however, to integrate the two fields, inward and outward, into one, by selecting elements from both for simultaneous attention. When the two fields are integrated in this way, the stimulus pattern and the response pattern can be recorded within the same spotlight of attention so that cause-and-effect relations between them can be perceived.

When you start making observations in this way you discover that your sensations of muscular tension, heaviness, stiffness and their opposites are not chaotic and meaningless but have a central pattern which changes in response to the changing pattern of stimuli from without or to the changing thought-images or "free-associations" within. Finding this pattern is like finding the clue that leads out of a maze. It introduces order where confusion prevailed.

If a response is delayed, as it is in waiting for a light to change in traffic, you are often aware that muscular tension is building up in preparation for the movement to come. Preparatory activity or "set" is presumably present before all learned responses, whether delayed or not. A set in this sense of the term is an attitude of expectancy which facilities a learned response. You are most apt to become aware of a set when the expected does not occur as when a shovel full of snow is heavier than it looks, or there is one less stair to climb than you anticipated.

Sets differ from one another according to the expected character (the "idea") of the response and the previous experience of the subject. There are sets for speaking; for picking up a pencil; for getting up from a chair; for smoking a cigarette; for playing the piano. Sets speed the response and make it easier to carry out automatically. They do not always make the response better, however. Sometimes they get in the way. This is especially noticeable in complex, sequential activities. A pianist may blur the execution of a measure because he is already getting set for the next. Or a string-player may have difficulty bowing because he becomes set too soon for the reverse movement of the bow. So in reading aloud the eye may get ahead of the speech organs and impose a set for another word before the first has been completely articulated.

A set may be imposed very quickly after the stimulus is given, but it is never instantaneous. It starts with a change in tonus or tensional balance in the neck and trunk and spreads from there to the limbs so that there is a general postural change before the particular goal-directed part of the pattern appears.[3]

The postural component can best be studied in another response pattern, a pattern which is not goal-directed and is presumably un-learned. In response to a sudden loud noise an involuntary postural change takes place. Though the response is sometimes over in half a second it has a regular time sequence, starting in the muscles of the face and neck and passing down the body. When it is complete it always involves the muscles of the neck.[4] Without them apparently the response cannot be propagated, or spread.

The pattern of startle (which has been studied by high-speed photography) is remarkably regular.[5] It begins with an eye-blink; the head is then thrust forward; the shoulders are raised and the arms stiffened; abdominal muscles shorten; breathing stops and the knees are flexed. The pattern permits minor variations but its primary features are the same. Because the startle response is brief and unexpected, it is difficult to observe and more difficult to control. Its chief interest here lies in the fact that it is a model of other, slower response patterns:[6] fear, anxiety, fatigue and pain all show postural changes from the norm which are similar to those that are seen in startle. In all of them there is a shortening of neck muscles which displaces the head, and which is usually followed by some kind of flexion response, so that the body is drawn into a slightly smaller space. As in startle these postural responses cannot take place without the prior displacement of the head and the shortening of neck muscles. Since these responses are much slower than the startle response, they can be changed by controlling the first stage in the pattern, the head displacement, through which the rest of the pattern is propagated. Changing a response pattern in this way is quite different from suppressing it or ignoring the stimulus, which may well call for a response. Changing the postural pattern simply insures that the response will be rational and appropriate to the situation instead of an irrational stereotype. By reorganizing the field of attention both phases of the response pattern are taken in at the same time. The goal-directed phase, (the learned part of the pattern) is allowed to continue, while the set is controlled by the method which I have described. Awareness of the head–neck–trunk relation serves as a framework for the learned activity. By inhibiting the set or fixation of the head, a better distribution of tonus is obtained in the trunk and limbs and better coordination and control of the specific activity, whether it is speaking, or writing or playing the flute.

Elsewhere[7] I have advanced the view that the physiological mechanism which makes these effects possible is the head–neck reflexes, which integrate and modulate the response of the organism to gravity. Briefly, release of neck-muscle tension, allowing surface muscles in the neck to lengthen, increases the anti-gravity response in postural muscles; shortening the same muscles decreases the strength of the response. It is well established that head–neck reflexes are used by animals to change the distribution of tonus in the trunk and limbs and that the same mechanism probably operates in human beings.

It is unnecessary, however, to *know* why the mechanism works in order to use it. The chief difficulty lies in the fact that we are not accustomed to making kinaesthetic observations and prefer to accept the evidence of our other senses or somebody else's judgement rather than critically examine our feelings of tension and weight. The only satisfactory technique I know for dealing with this problem was devised by F. M. Alexander[8] some sixty years ago. By watching himself in a triple-mirror, Alexander was able to correlate changes in the axis of his head with a loss of voice in speaking. He found that by inhibiting the change in head-axis he not only regained the use of his voice but produced an unexpected redistribution of tension throughout his body which brought with it an improvement in breathing and other automatic functions. For imparting his discovery to others, he developed a non-verbal technique which is referred to as the Alexander Technique. In it the pupil learns to inhibit any tendency he may have to alter the reflex balance of his head, while the teacher initiates some simple, everyday movement and guides the pupil through to its completion. Any movement will do: walking, shifting position in a chair, getting up and sitting down, picking up a pencil. During this kind of movement (which should be called "reflex facilitated," rather than active or passive) postural tonus is redistributed. This is perceived by the subject as a reduction in the feeling of weight and in the effort needed to move. This kinaesthetic effect persists long enough after a lesson to give the pupil an opportunity to observe his own habitual actions against a new background of postural tonus. In this way he gradually builds up a standard of kinaesthetic judgement for himself and can go on to make further observations and experiments of his own. In doing so he has added greatly to his resources for self-improvement.

It should be possible to make the necessary first observations without help from outside—it has been done at least once before—but most people lack the patience and insight to do so without instruction. Fortunately, instruction is easier to obtain than it once was.

To end with a quotation from the Greeks, Sophocles said:

> The ideal condition would be, I admit,
> That man should be right by instinct;
> But since we are all too likely to go astray
> The reasonable thing is to learn from those who can teach.[9]

1. William James, *Principles of Psychology* (New York: Henry Holt, 1890), Vol. 1, pp. 403–404.

2. J. J. Gibson, *The Senses Considered as Perceptual Systems* (Boston, Mass.: Houghton Mifflin Co., 1966), p. 44.

3. Frank P. Jones, "The Influence of Postural Set on Pattern of Movement of Man." *International Journal of Neurology*, 4 (1963), pp. 60–71.

4. Frank P. Jones and John L. Kennedy, "An Electromyographic Technique for Recording the Startle Pattern." *Journal of Psychology*, 32 (1951), pp. 63–68.

5. Carney Landis and William A. Hunt, *The Startle Pattern* (New York: Farrar and Rinehart, 1939).

6. Frank P. Jones, John A. Hanson and Florence E. Gray, "Startle as a Paradigm of Malposture." *Perceptual and Motor Skills*, 19 (1964), pp. 21–22.

7. Frank P. Jones, "A Method for Changing Stereotyped Response Patterns by the Inhibition of Certain Postural Sets." *Psychological Review*, 72 (May 1965), pp. 196–214.

8. F. Matthlas Alexander, *The Use of the Self* (New York: Dutton, 1932).

9. Dudley Fitts and Robert Fitzgerald, *The Antigone of Sophocles* (New York: Harcourt, Brace & Co., 1939), p. 48.

Appendix C

Awareness, Freedom and Muscular Control

THERE ARE MUSICIANS—some say there were more of them in the past—who get as much pleasure from a performance as they give, who always perform easily and well, and who use themselves so efficiently that their professional lives and their natural lives coincide. There are others, however, with equal talent and training, to whom performance and even practice are exhausting, and whose professional lives are cut short because they lose the mastery of the skills they have acquired. They put forth more effort in solving technical problems than the results warrant, and ultimately discover that they have used up their reserves of energy. If they understood the use of themselves as well as they understand the use of their instruments, such breakdowns would be far less frequent.

In practice and performance, however, a musician's attention is given almost exclusively to what he is doing with his hands or his feet or his vocal organs, and to the sounds they are producing. Of what he is doing with the rest of his body, he usually knows very little. In attacking a difficult problem of technique, the average performer uses two approaches: He "tries hard" to master it, using all the skill at his command; and if his trying builds up too much tension and fatigues him, he "relaxes." In both cases he is working on a trial-and-error basis. He has no way of knowing exactly how much tension is needed, or how to limit it to the time and place where it is wanted.

To take a concrete example, a double-bass player, in order to get the force and control he wanted for finishing the downstroke of his

Reprinted from *Musical America*, January 1, 1949.

bow, habitually built up so much misdirected tension in his arm that he could not start the upstroke smoothly. Furthermore, he built up a corresponding overtension in other parts of his body—his back, neck and legs. Since he concentrated his attention upon his arms and hands, he was unaware what was happening elsewhere until it showed up in the form of pain and fatigue.

Any performer who continues in this way runs the risk of becoming progressively more muscle-bound, and of losing his freedom of movement. If he recognizes the trouble and attempts to remedy it by relaxing, he runs into the danger in reverse. Either he becomes limp and relatively incompetent, or in achieving relaxation in one part he pays for it by becoming overtense somewhere else. I know a pianist who succeeded in getting almost complete freedom in her arms, so that her fingers showed a truly remarkable sensitivity and power of fluent movement. But in the process she developed an extraordinary amount of tension in her neck and an aching heaviness in her back and legs. Her attention was given exclusively to her arms and hands, and she did not realize that what she was doing with the rest of her body exhausted her.

It has often been said that our senses deceive us. This statement is especially true of the sense of muscular movement, or kinaesthesia. Often it can be shown that a person is doing something quite different from what he thinks he is doing. A pianist, for example, once complained to me that in playing he had a sense of great weakness in his hands, which increased whenever he struck certain chords, until it seemed as though he scarcely had the strength to push down the keys. I discovered that just at the moment of attack he was tightening the muscles of his lower arms in such a way that his hands were actually drawn back from the keys. To overcome this backward pull and strike the chord, he had to exert a tremendous amount of force. What he sensed was resistance in the keys and weakness in his hands. The cause, which he failed to recognize, was misdirected strength. As in the other examples which I have cited, the muscular misuse was not confined to his arms and hands. He "got set" all over, with an increase of tension through his neck, shoulders and back, so that the tension in his lower arms was literally "locked in" from above. The amount of tension and the pattern of its distribution were determined by his past experiences in using his arms, both in play-

Freedom to Change

ing the piano and in other activities, and he did not know that there was any other way of using them.

In most cases, I am convinced that it is futile to attack these problems directly, because the use of the hand or any other part of the body is so closely linked to the manner in which the body as a whole is used. But if a person can be made aware of his muscular movements as a whole, and learn to distinguish their general, overall pattern, he can make constructive changes and corrections on the basis of knowledge rather than of trial and error. Armed with this knowledge, a musician can become, in effect, his own "expert."

This new approach to the problem of change has been made possible by an important discovery F. Matthias Alexander, of London, made about the nature of reflex action. To my knowledge, Alexander was the first expert, working with human beings in ordinary activities of life, to show and prove that there is what he called the "primary control" within each individual. He defines the primary control as "a certain use of the head and neck in relation to the rest of the body." By observation and experiment upon himself, "using," as John Dewey said, "the strictest scientific method," he learned that the mechanism that determines the character of all reflex action lies in the reflexes governing the relation of the head to the neck. When the primary control is functioning as it should, it is sensed as an integrating force that preserves freedom of movement throughout the system, so that energy can be directed to the place where it is wanted without developing strain either there or elsewhere. Misuse of the primary control, on the other hand, is always reflected by misuse somewhere else; this appears in the form of awkwardness, fatigue and what Wilfred Barlow, a London physician and a pupil of Alexander, calls "maldistributed muscle tension," or overtension at one place accompanied by undertension (lack of tone) at another.

G. E. Coghill, the American biologist, has pointed out that Alexander's findings agree with what is known of animal movement in general. The importance of the head in animal movement is well known, and the dominance of the head–neck reflexes in the reflex pattern was established experimentally by Rudolph Magnus and his co-workers.

Alexander showed that in human beings under civilized conditions the head–neck relationship is unconsciously interfered with, to a greater or less degree. His great contribution to education was the discovery of a means by which a person can become aware of this interference and regain the normal use of the primary control. From this discovery and the deductions he made from it, Alexander established, as Bernard Shaw said in the introduction to the volume entitled *London Music*, "the beginnings of a far-reaching science of the apparently involuntary movements we call reflexes." John Dewey, who introduced Alexander's work in this country, said that the discovery was "as important as any principle that has ever been discovered in the domain of external nature."

The principal is general in its application, and not confined to the problems of musicians. In my experience, however, musicians have been unusually quick to grasp its significance and put it to practical use. Perhaps this is because musicians as a class are keenly aware of the kinaesthetic side of experience. In this article I have directed attention to the problems of instrumentalists; but the principle can be used equally effectively by singers and conductors. Sir Adrian Boult studied with Alexander in London, and many singers have made use of his teaching. The value to singers lies in the fact that the primary control, when it is functioning as it should, prevents interference in the reflexes that control the vocal organs and the breathing mechanism. In this connection, it should be noted that Alexander made his original discovery when he was seeking to find the cause of his own loss of voice in speaking. An account of his procedure is given in *The Use of the Self* (1932).

In teaching the principle to a musician (or to anyone else, for that matter), the aim is to increase the pupil's awareness of himself as a whole, until he can detect the interference in the head–neck relationship, which is the first link in the reflex chain of "getting set" to do something—to sit down, to pick up a bow or to strike a chord. In order to accomplish this, the teacher helps the pupil to carry out the activity without the habitual interference, and to realize by actual experience the lightness and freedom of movement that come when the primary control operates normally. Through repeated experience of this kind, the pupil gradually builds a new standard of kinaesthetic judgement. With this standard he has the power at any time to *know* whether he is obtaining the maximum of freedom and control in what he is doing. If he is not obtaining it he learns how to find the cause of the trouble and eliminate it.

Because the principle is general in its application, a musician is learning something he can use to advantage in whatever he is doing. And conversely, his improved use of himself in everyday life will be reflected in his music. The double-bass player of my first illustration reported, as the first tangible results of his lessons, that he had mowed the lawn without tiring his back, and had kept his equanimity while asking trespassers to leave his property. The same kind of conscious control appeared in his playing and in the ease with which he learned to adapt himself to the demands of his instrument.

I have not meant to suggest that a primary knowledge of the primary control can take the place of natural talent or eliminate the need for technical training and practice. But as a complement to professional study, the musician will find the knowledge invaluable. Over a period of years I have watched the progress of musicians who have learned to use this new approach to their problems, and have witnessed the increasing gain it has brought them in ease of performance, lessened fatigue, and the confidence that comes with a true self-knowledge.

Appendix D

Learning How to Learn: An Operational Definition of the Alexander Technique

I DO NOT OFTEN HAVE the opportunity to talk about the Alexander Technique to an audience that already knows what it is and does not have to be convinced of its importance. Usually the people I talk to have never heard of the Technique or, if they have heard of it, have confused it with something else. The second group is becoming more common.

In the United States there has been a great proliferation of mind-body techniques and therapies. Some profess to heal the body by way of the mind, others the mind by way of the body.

There are spiritual disciplines, exercise programmes, relaxation techniques. Some use massage (in all its varieties), some use hypnosis and autohypnosis. Some heighten your body-awareness by getting you to concentrate on specific areas of tension. Some use breathing exercises: some use group experiences to release emotional blocks, by chanting, by touching, by giving your first impressions of the others in the group. There are also techniques for stimulating the imagination by acting out your daydreams and fantasies. One hundred and five of these techniques are listed by Severin Peterson in his book *Ways People Grow.* They are listed alphabetically from Aikido to Zen. All of these methods claim to make you more of a "whole person" and add to your physical and emotional health. Most of them are organized as separate disciplines, each somewhat defensive towards the others. Recently, however, there has been a trend toward eclecticism, and therapists are appearing who encourage their pa-

---

Paper read at the Constructive Teaching Centre, London, June 25, 1973.

tients to combine several of these methods in a kind of package deal. Sometimes the Alexander Technique is part of the package. It is listed second by Peterson right after Aikido.

I suppose one should feel grateful at being invited into the therapeutic club.

The invitation presents new problems, however. In my opinion Alexander did not discover just another way to achieve individual salvation. His technique (or principle) is on a different level or order of significance from the other "ways to grow," which are all, as far as I have been able to determine, simply variations on an old theme. Alexander's discovery (as Dewey pointed out) is comparable to the discoveries that were made in the Renaissance and that caused men to change their ideas of external nature. When you look through a microscope or a telescope the first time you are forced, if you accept the evidence of your senses, to revise your views of the universe outside yourself. Alexander discovered a way of using his hands to give a person new experiences which force him to revise his ideas both of himself and of the universe. Of course a person can reject the experience just as the Professor of Philosophy at Padua rejected Galileo's hypothesis by refusing to look through the telescope. The important thing is that the experience is now available, thanks to F. M.'s discovery. (Here let me say that I do not mean the discovery he made with the mirror. Others may have done the same thing. I mean the discovery that he could communicate his new experiences to others by using his hands.) The discovery has profound implications. If the new knowledge were properly formulated, I believe that it would do for the field of psychology what Newton did for physics, transform it into a unified science. No Newton has come along as yet. In the meantime, I feel that the rest of us are under an obligation to keep the incipient science alive and not allow it to be swallowed up by other means and ends before its true potential has been realized and its unique value as an educational discipline established.

With this aim in mind, I should like to sketch for your consideration some of the aspects of the Alexander Technique which in my opinion make it different from anything else.

First I'd like to say that there are two effects of the Technique which should not be used as criteria, impressive though they are.

One is improvement in health and the other is improvement in posture.

Most pupils when they start having lessons are struck by the improvement in their health and refer to this improvement when they try to describe the Technique to their friends. I have heard Alexander pupils say that the Technique saved their vision, or saved their career, saved their reason, or saved their life. No doubt it did. Unfortunately, similar claims have been made for almost anything you can think of. It is always difficult to prove that your results followed directly from the means employed and could not have come about in any other way. I reluctantly came to this conclusion a long time ago when I got two badly crippled children to walk—this was in a hospital and the process was observed by four doctors and several nurses. Everyone was pleased with the results. They explained them, however, by saying that I had used suggestion to restore the children's confidence in themselves. The children were then turned over to physiotherapists to continue the good work.

Case histories are important and do throw light on the mechanisms involved in the Technique. But they confuse by overstressing the medical aspect. The Technique can profitably be taught to anybody; it is not restricted in its application to people with disabilities. When I began teaching, all of my pupils had serious health problems, and lessons made them feel better. When I went to Tufts, I was afraid it would be difficult working with students who had no serious health problems. This did not prove to be the case, and I was forced to revise my ideas and methods of teaching since I found that "normal" subjects demanded a different approach.

Posture is another criterion which seems promising at first but must, I believe, be rejected (if by posture you mean the three-dimensional arrangement of the parts of the body which can be recorded by instantaneous photography). Everyone has an idea of what "bad" posture is (though "good" posture is more difficult to define). After lessons in the Alexander Technique bad posture usually improves in a striking way, and it may be useful to take photographs before and after a course of lessons to demonstrate the improvement. Unfortunately again, practitioners of other methods produce similar before-and-after photographs, and it would be difficult to prove from the photographs alone that their results are inferior to those achieved by the Alexander Technique. I once showed some of these still photographs to a doctor at Harvard and he assured me that in the Physical Education Department they made these changes all the time.

If you cannot use posture as a criterion, then what can you use? I believe that the distinguishing criterion should be the movement pattern itself. As I understand it, the Alexander Technique is not concerned with three-dimensional but with four-dimensional posture, in other words with movement. A. R. Alexander refused to judge a person's posture as good or bad until he had seen him move or until he had put his hands on him. I have seen the magnificent posture disintegrate in an instant. Athletes and dancers can go into a postural collapse when they are through performing. On the other hand, I have seen people with atrocious posture who move quite easily, and as they moved their posture improved. An American college professor who was a pupil of the Alexanders during the war had a posture that could not be changed. He was an arthritic; his spinal column was ankylosed and his head fixed in position. As you can imagine, he was a difficult pupil, but the Alexanders (the two of them worked with him together) succeeded in teaching him, and he profited tremendously from the Technique. Still photographs, however, would not have recorded the change.

Movement photographs are different. With either motion-picture or multiple-strobe photography you can obtain a record of the trajectory (or pathway) followed by the head during a movement. By measuring the area underneath this trajectory you obtain an index of the efficiency of the movement from the Alexander point of view, since the area increases when the neck and back are allowed to lengthen. The increase in "working height" or "moving height," unlike the static height of a postural photograph, cannot, I feel sure, be faked or obtained by non-Alexandrian methods of exercise or relaxation. Combined with the subjective report of a reduction in the effort expended to move, it gives an index of efficiency which, to my knowledge, nothing but the Alexander Technique can produce. The index can be applied to a great many everyday movements—sitting-to-standing, walking, stairclimbing, picking up objects and the like. I have not tried to record skilled movements like those of a dancer but I am sure the same index can be used with them.

(I should say here that I do not use photographs of this kind in my teaching but have found them invaluable for scientific purposes.)

Believing that the significant aspect of the Technique is not posture but movement, I do not like to make a pupil self-conscious about postural faults. In my observation this promotes anxiety—what the Alexanders called "trying to be right"—and interferes with the learning process. Using the Alexander principle you can get the pupil to move in a non-habitual and easier way. As he does so his posture will change and many specific faults will be reduced. This experience should register kinaesthetically to the pupil as pleasanter, more efficient and more desirable than his habitual way of moving. It should, in Skinnerian terminology, be reinforcing. It can give the pupil a new insight into his own use and functioning without having his postural faults pointed out to him.

I have had interesting accounts of such experiences from some of the students at Tufts who studied the Technique for various reasons. Two of them were athletes, one a hammer thrower and the other a distance runner. The hammer thrower kept a journal of his experiences, starting with his first lesson. He made a number of interesting observations, the most interesting having to do with his specialty. He knew that he was doing something with his shoulder that interfered with his throw; the coach had pointed it out to him; and he had seen himself doing it on a television play-back; but he could not make a change during his performance. With lessons he found that he could perceive kinaesthetically what he was doing wrong and inhibit it; and he was able in this way to add six feet to his maximum throw. This happened quite early in lessons. The journal entries from this point on increase in interest as he notes his tendency to turn his knowledge "into a doing" (as the Alexanders used to say) and as he realizes that the Technique, if it is going to give him full value, has to be applied to everything, not just to athletic performance.

The other athlete was not so highly motivated. He was the champion runner at the school and had no particular interest in improving his performance. He noticed, however, that he was getting less and less satisfaction out of running and found himself increasingly fatigued at the end of a race. He had only a few lessons and apparently got what he wanted from them. His report is also interesting.

He told me that after a lesson, he had run in an important race. As long as he was unsure of winning, he was unable to release the excess tension in his neck, though he was sharply aware of it. As soon, however, as he was comfortably ahead of his rivals he found that he could stop what he was doing with his neck and finished the race exhilarated rather than exhausted.

This was the first time I had ever worked with athletes, but from these two experiences I would conclude that track performance is a natural field for demonstrating the Alexander principle, since the results can be so readily quantified. It is subjective reports, however, rather than the end results that throw the most light on the principle. What distinguishes the Alexander Technique from all other methods of self-improvement that I know anything about is the character of the thinking involved. Other people talk about awareness and thinking, but operationally they mean something quite different from the Alexander experience. To me it is an expansion of the field of consciousness (or of "attention" if you object to the term consciousness") in space and in time so that you are taking in both yourself and your environment, both the present moment and the next. It is a unified field organized around the self as a centre. At the beginning it has a very simple system of organization but it always takes in both the self (including the relation of the head to the trunk) and something in the environment. In addition to the head relation you can take in the pressure of your feet against the floor and also the pressure of the floor against your feet; you can take in both your eyes and the object you are looking at; your ears and the sounds you are hearing. You can take in what you are doing now and what you are going to do next, without getting tangled up in the process. The expansion of awareness in time restores free will as a datum of experience.

Such a concept of awareness would, if it were established, force the re-organization of two fields of psychology—perception, which at present is fractionated, and learning-theory, which seems unable to cope with the problem of free will.

The expanded field of consciousness makes possible what Dewey called "thinking in activity." In my experience the field cannot be maintained for any great span of time (though I have found that the span steadily increases over the years). It fades in and fades out. When it has faded out for any length of time, its absence manifests itself by a sense of nagging discomfort which forces one back to the "means whereby."

I believe that this model can be applied to any situation that involves perception or learning. A good illustration was supplied by another student who was an accomplished jazz musician. His specialty was "miscellaneous percussion"; that is, he had at his disposal a large variety of instruments which could be struck, pounded, shaken, rattled or scraped. Jazz, as he explained it to me, is wholly improvisational. The jazz musician has to be aware of what he is doing, what he is going to do next and what everyone else in the band is doing, without losing feedback from the audience. He must be able, my student wrote, "to conceive and execute his own ideas while keeping the music that is coming at him as a reference." This, he added, "is nothing more than maintaining a balance between internal and external environment." "Self-monitoring" is the term he used to describe this ability. If you do not have it instinctively, he said, the Alexander Technique is the only way to get it.

I'd like to read this to you in his own words: "The major problem that one has when starting out on an instrument is the inability to monitor your own performance. Again the invaluable nature of the Alexander Technique as applied to music instruction is apparent. The more one becomes aware of physical counterparts to seemingly unrelated phenomena the more objective one can be in viewing one's own workings, due to the objective sensory distance that prevents one from interfering with the task. A good student even when operating under the auspices of a teacher must always fill in between the teacher's words of wisdom. You cannot *teach* anybody anything; but you can teach them how to learn."

"Learning how to learn" is what distinguishes the Alexander Technique from all the other "ways to grow." Thinking, directing, "giving orders," or however you wish to describe it, is not an end in itself. It has value and meaning only as it is applied to the pupil's own life. As Marjorie Barstow, an American teacher who was in Alexander's first training course, put it: "giving orders is a procedure that turns into activity, not (into) fixtures; the teacher is only a guide to help the student learn to think and do for himself; it is the teacher's job to help the student carry on into daily activities."

Appendix E

Drafts and Notes

WHEN I STARTED THIS book I said that I would distinguish the Alexander Technique from the other mind-body therapies and "ways to grow" that now compete for the attention of the public. It is not a substitute for any of them—though there are some educational and therapeutic procedures, both orthodox and unorthodox, that are not in conflict with the Alexander Technique and might usefully be combined with it. There is none that accomplishes the same result. If it does the same thing it is the Alexander Technique and differs only in name. After searching for thirty years I have not discovered anything that does.

In summarizing my account here I shall confine myself to those properties of the Technique that are not to be found elsewhere. It only causes confusion to describe an educational system by delineating results which have been forcefully claimed for half a dozen competing systems. The two criteria that are most frequently used are improvement in health and improvement in posture. Neither is sufficient in itself to distinguish the Technique from other systems. Evidence could easily be assembled to document cases of spectacular recovery from a variety of disabilities. I know of pupils who would be happy to testify that a knowledge of the Technique saved their vision, saved their career, saved their reason or saved their life. I do not doubt that it did. But equally spectacular claims have been made for almost every variety of orthodox and unorthodox treatment.

Editor's note: These sections have been edited from an outline of a fifteenth chapter and notes from a journal. They have been arranged thematically.

The same thing is true of posture, if by posture is meant the three-dimensional arrangement of parts of the body that can be recorded by instantaneous photography. Everyone has an idea of what "bad" posture is—"good" posture, on the other hand, is more difficult to define. After lessons in the Alexander Technique bad posture usually improves in a striking way and it might be instructive to take a set of photographs before and after lessons. Unfortunately such photographs have been used to prove the efficacy of everything from structural integration to the latest charm school. The fact is that postural change is an "accident" not a "property" of the Alexander Technique. It has meaning only in so far as it reflects a change in movement pattern or, more fundamentally, a change in the manner of responding to stimuli.

To distinguish the Alexander Technique from the 134 "Ways to Grow" what are its "properties" as opposed to its "accidents"?

Accidents

1. It is not "curative". It is preventive. "Cures" may take place in process but they are not aimed for.
2. It is not a way of achieving "good" posture.
3. It is not a "treatment."
4. It makes no use of suggestion. You can't convey a sensory experience to someone who has never had it by describing it to him—i.e., by telling a blind man what something looks like.
5. It does not have adverse side effects.
6. It is not a "relaxation technique."
7. It is not concerned with remote causes, genetic factors, early experiences or even medical history.

Properties

1. It is concerned with a real, demonstrable physiological mechanism.
2. It changes the pattern of movement and the manner of responding to stimuli (changes the acceleration curve).
3. It is concerned with the organization of awareness.
4. It is concerned with "non-doing"—inhibition.

5. It is not a mass solution. The Technique can appeal only to the individual who wants to change.
6. It satisfies the "need for competence".
7. It facilitates "insight learning."
8. It is consistent with any therapy or educational procedure which is specific. It is inconsistent with suggestion, auto-suggestion, hypnosis, drugs (in general) and alcohol (in general).
9. It brings into learning some of the pleasure and excitement which children feel when they do things for the first time—and begin to explore the world.
10. It produces (or induces) gradual change.
11. It forces a person to accept responsibility for his own salvation.
12. It brings up the concept of "cognitive dissonance." When you have been finally forced to accept the proposition that you can change, the question then comes up: should I change?
13. It is a means for dealing with change—but change based on a knowledge of reality. Freedom to change, but first you have to know and accept yourself for what you are.

It would be invidious and not very instructive to compare the Alexander Technique to the other systems individually. Differences can be summed up under one rubric. The Alexander Technique is concerned only with means—to F. M. it was a "means-whereby" technique while all others were "end-gaining." How to distinguish the Alexander Technique from other means of salvation: not by end-result—e.g. improvement in health, posture and performance, but by three characteristics which are not found elsewhere: a) kinaesthetic perception, b) primary control, and c) inhibition.

Because of its emphasis on attention, movement and the present moment, the Alexander Technique can easily be and often has been confused with the many fashionable awareness techniques—Eastern and Western. One is especially reminded of the Alexander Technique when reading about Gestalt Therapy. This is not a coincidence since Fritz Perls, the father of Gestalt, was strongly influenced by Alexander. Perls brought analysis out of the unconscious, away from abstractions into the concrete present. He made his patients aware of what they were doing now and of how they were doing it. He went beyond verbal content to the voice itself and to posture and movement. He attacked intellectualizing, free associating and mind wandering as false solutions. He stressed seeing and hearing and forced his patients to be aware of what they were doing, to face the reality of anxiety and pain.

On kinaesthesia

The Alexander Technique is a method for organizing your kinaesthetic impressions—your sensations of movement, of position, of tension and weight—into a more unified system and adding to the efficiency and ease of everyday activity.

I can't talk about the Alexander Technique without using the word "kinaesthesia". So I'll start out by defining it. Kinaesthesia is a Greek word—it is too bad there isn't a good English word for it like "sight" or "hearing" or "touch"—it means literally "the sensation of movement" but it is used to cover sensations of position, weight and tension as well. It gives you information about yourself as opposed to information about your environment. Aristotle did not list it among his five senses and it has received very little attention in textbooks of sensory psychology. From a practical point of view, however, kinaesthesia is the most important sense of all. It is the one sense you can't get along without.

It has been recognized from the time of Plato that the senses are unreliable. No one, however, (before F. M. Alexander) made the obvious inference that, since this is the case, it is necessary to restore this reliability before progress is possible—indeed that it must be restored to prevent further degeneration. Instead they have sought something else on which knowledge may be based—faith, authority, mysticism or pure reason. Our senses, however, are our only means for finding out the state not only of the external world but of ourselves. Our intelligence has shown us that they cannot be depended upon; we must use our intelligence to restore their dependability.

It is generally recognized that excessive tension is an evil and is to be avoided. The only standard offered, however, is the individual's own feelings. In studying the physical world investigators long ago decided that the senses were untrustworthy. Examples are easy to find. In estimating temperature, for instance, the feelings of the individual are notoriously deceptive. Scientists solved the difficulty by working out methods of comparing the variation of two substances in response to the same stimulus. When there is found a definite correlation one activity is said to be a function of the other and the statement of how they vary is called a scientific law. An example is the mercury thermometer in which the height of a given column of mercury varies directly with the temperature. Alexander teaches the pupil to use a similar device in measuring tension throughout his system.

Stiffening the neck is in some degree a constant in everyone and because it is constant the individual is not aware of it, just as one is unaware of a constant velocity when travelling. Acceleration (or deceleration) reaches the consciousness. So in the Alexander work the pupil must first be made aware of the increase of tension that accompanies activity. It is only after noticing this increase that he can become aware of the ordinary tension.

Alexander realized that the mechanism he had uncovered was what controlled the distribution of muscle tonus throughout the system, and, if it was interfered with (as it had been in his case), tonus would be maldistributed in one way or another.

In working out a method for conveying his experience to his pupils he found that the big stumbling block was sensory deception—the feeling that you've got to do something the way you have always done it before.

He solved the problem by using his hands to change the pupil's postural set—by preventing change in the head-trunk axis—while the pupil carried out the activity in question—in this way the pupil has the experience of doing something he knows how to do but doing it without the effort he has used before—after you have had the experience you learn how you did it—but the experience always comes first and learning second (this can be perplexing at first to a person whose learning has largely been verbal learning).

When Alexander demonstrated the Technique to me I noticed a number of changes that seemed to be taking place more or less at the same time—one of them (the one I was hoping for) was a change in breathing—the most striking change to me, however, was a decrease in the feeling of weight and the effort needed to move. I remember thinking at the time that it was as if I had been wearing a lead-lined shirt all my life and had suddenly lost it.

The decrease in the feeling of weight, in my opinion, is the key to the experience. It is my theory that what Alexander discovered in himself, and later in others, was an interference in the anti-gravity reflexes—and that the anti-gravity reflexes are the mechanism that integrates all other reflex systems.

In my view, what Alexander discovered, and was able by his technique to correct, was an interference in the anti-gravity response system—that system of reflexes which brings an animal up in the gravitational field, which maintains tonus in muscles and fluid in joints and facilitates both posture and movement. Without such a system, the animals never would have gotten out of the sea. When it works as it should, it not only orients the animal to its environment but, as its name implies, effectively counteracts gravity so that there is no inertia to overcome to initiate a voluntary movement.

On different views of the Alexander Technique

Question: How do you account for the varied points of view about the Alexander work, ranging from improved posture to a philosophy of life?

Answer: I account for the variety in two ways:

1) Some people read F. M. Alexander's books or have a few demonstration lessons and are fired with enthusiasm for a vague, general idea of "non-doing" or "not end-gaining" which they deduce from their experience. Others close their minds to the possibility of a new experience and refuse to see anything in the work but a kind of posture training, yoga, or whatever association of ideas suggests itself to them. Both interpretations miss the significance of the work completely. You can be wrong about something in a great variety of ways.

2) In a sense, there is also a great variety of ways in which you can be "right." Understanding the significance of the principle of the primary control and applying it, no matter how partially, to the solution of practical problems inevitably bring about a change in habitual patterns of reacting to stimuli. Depending upon the resources of the person, how far he is willing to apply the principle and how long he lives, there is no limit to the extent to which not only his life but his philosophy of life may be affected. As the range of his experience and control extends he will continually revise and

enlarge his understanding of the principle. Consequently, there is bound to be a great range of opinion, even among those who rightly grasp the basic principle. To some, it will mean no more than improved posture and lessened fatigue. I see no reason for quarrelling with this point of view, since both are definite, tangible goods. What is of more importance to me, however, is the possibility of change in moral and mental attitude and the extension of the range within which free choice and free will can operate.

On primary control

The primary control is a dynamic relationship between the centre of gravity of the head and the vertebrae in the neck which allows the head to move in an orbit which promotes maximal lengthening of the spine and facilitates movement throughout the body. If this equilibrium of forces is perceived kinaesthetically the mechanism can be brought under conscious control by inhibiting the shortening of muscles that would displace the centre of gravity from its natural orbit.

The primary control can be defined in physiological terms. It is a basic feedback mechanism which facilitates both reflex and voluntary movement by maintaining an optimal distribution of postural tonus. It has the characteristics of all homeostatic systems. A system of forces is maintained in dynamic balance so that any disturbance in balance leading to overactivity or underactivity in the system is detected by sensors which send a signal into the display centre where it can be detected and a corrective response process initiated that will restore the balance. In man-made biofeedback systems the signal is displayed either visually or audibly. The subject learns by means of the feedback thus obtained to make a response that restores the balance to a previously defined level. Biofeedback training has been successfully used at least under laboratory conditions to establish a direct conscious control over various parts of the autonomic system. Patients have been trained to lower their blood pressure, decrease their heart rate, decrease the activity of sweat glands and change the frequency of their brain waves. The practical application of this kind of control has not yet been demonstrated, however. It differs radically from the inhibitory control over skeletal muscle which is established in the Alexander Technique.

In the Technique the signal denoting a disturbance in the balance of forces making up the postural system is displayed in the neck and back where it can be perceived kinaesthetically and inhibited, thus facilitating the operation of the system as a whole. Other forms of biofeedback are direct and specific. They cannot be successfully applied during physical or mental activity without interrupting the activity. For example it would not be feasible for a basketball player to lower his blood pressure during a game or a musician to change the frequency of his brain waves during a concert. The Alexander Technique, on the other hand, makes use of a control which, being indirect and inhibitory, can be established and maintained during any activity merely by expanding the field of consciousness.

Any activity is facilitated if the centre of gravity of the head moves forward while the head itself moves up.

On suggestion

The use of suggestion in teaching the Alexander Technique illustrates the adage "Nothing fails like success." It is possible and really very easy to suggest a sensory experience and have a pupil or even an observer report that he experiences it, but once a person has convinced himself he has had a sensory experience, whatever this experience is, he will keep on having it whether it is appropriate or not—after this it may become almost impossible to give him an authentic experience.

On conditioning

In teaching the Alexander Technique you are working directly with the stimulus–response pattern, and by changing the "manner of responding" you are indirectly affecting both the mind and the body.

Alexander discovered that between the stimulus and the response—any stimulus and any response—there is a characteristic "set" or preparation which determines the character and quality of the response. When you can perceive these "sets" kinaesthetically you have a means for altering the response.

In teaching the Alexander Technique you work directly with the stimulus–response pattern and, by changing "the manner of responding", indirectly affect both the body and the mind.

You do not use suggestion—in fact you lean over backward to avoid it—most people are far too susceptible as it is. You want them to observe something they have not observed before. Suggestions will only get in the way.

What do you want them to observe?—that little-known area between the stimulus and the response. It is difficult in the ordinary way to observe a well-learned response—attention is focused on the goal, not on the movement. If I ask you to pick up a pencil, it would be hard for you to describe the movement afterward, although you could probably describe the pencil. The movement is not what is most important, however, it is the "set" that precedes it.

You have here a simple mechanism of behavioural change that does not depend on conditioning. In the Alexander principle, free will—the freedom to choose—is an integral part of the system.

The Technique is not a conditioned response—in classical conditioning you are linking a new, unspecific stimulus (the sound of the bell) to an old, well-established stimulus–response complex (sight of food→salivation), with the result that the new stimulus elicits the old response without the intervention of the old stimulus. I don't see how this model can apply to learning the Alexander Technique.

In visual perception, the image comes first: after it is discriminated, it is named. In teaching the Alexander Technique, the same sequence must be followed—Barlow reverses it. Another objection to Barlow's procedure is that there is no way of learning what part of the experience is conditioned to the words used. Something happens as a result of the manipulation—the experience is associated with the pupil's order—how does the pupil transfer this association to activity which he initiates?

In the Alexander Technique an old, familiar stimulus (the thought of standing up, or speaking) which elicits an old, well-established response, signals the subject to inhibit his old familiar response (tightening neck muscles) and permits a new, unfamiliar response to take place.

In my model, the field of attention is expanded to take in both the self and the environment—the stimulus and the response. When the two are perceived simultaneously, cause and effect relations (stimulus–response relations) can be understood operationally and a change introduced. In *Psychology Today* the Alexander Technique has been defined as "a method for improving posture by subtle suggestions and gentle manipulations". It is not a form of posture training and it does not use suggesting in any of its forms. People are far too suggestible anyway, and I am opposed to any method for increasing susceptibility or making good behaviour dependent an conditioning.

I disagree with Skinner that the world can be saved by giving up the illusion of free-will and by conditioning right responses with suitable "schedules of reinforcement".

If Skinner is right that there is no such thing as free will then we are stuck with a set of very maladapative responses, because I can't see how physical education, psychiatry or behavioural therapy as I understand it can do much for us at this stage. I don't think that he is right, however. I believe that we do have free will and that we can change our own behaviour if we want to. I believe with John Dewey, however, that we have to use our own intelligence and not go on depending an outside experts to tell us what to do. I will end up with a quote from Socrates: For a human being, an unexamined life is not worth living.

On education

All systems of education in the past have been based on the principle of "doing". The student has been taught or permitted to learn for himself a variety of particular skills or fields of knowledge. In every instance he has been either forced or encouraged to "do" something in order to attain a particular goal. And it has been assumed that if sufficient effort was put forth by teacher and pupil, the pupil would master the task set for him and might possibly go on by himself to attain further knowledge or skill in the same or other fields. The logic behind this assumption is fallacious: in the first place, the principle cannot be generalized and predictions cannot be based upon it; the same thing cannot be taught to all pupils with the same degree of success; some will learn it and some will not, but which ones these will be cannot be predicted with any degree of accuracy; nor is it possible in evaluating the results of teaching to determine what proportion of a success is due to the skill of the teacher and what to the innate capacity of the pupil; furthermore, because of individual differences it is impossible to imitate another person exactly, and, for this reason too, it is impossible to make any predictions about teaching based on the principle of "doing".

These objections do not hold for the opposite principle, that of "non-doing." It is possible to teach anyone how not to do whatever interferes with the efficient attainment of any goal in activity. Here individual differences are of small importance and in the matter of "non-doing" exact imitation is quite possible. Hence the principle can be generalized and prediction can be based upon it. That this is true has been demonstrated in the work of F. M. Alexander.

Educationalists, no matter how much they disagree on aims and objectives, are agreed that there is nothing basically wrong with the subject upon which their theories are to be tried out—that the child, if given the right stimuli, will develop his potentialities to the full. Some would by suggestion, example and encouragement, assist nature to bring about an integrated development of the child's nature, while others insist that only by various "disciplines" can this result be attained. But both schools agree that if only the right things are done the educational problem will be solved. Because of this common easy assumption that, though there are many imperfections in the world, education at least is on the right track, it is perhaps inevitable that little attention should be paid to anyone who suggests that not only are educational systems wrong in detail but contemporary education in general is on the wrong track. That is the suggestion that has been made by F. M. Alexander and that is undoubtedly why his writings have been largely neglected. If he had advanced some new method of instruction that could without too much trouble be incorporated into the curriculum he would no doubt, in view of his distinguished backing, have been accepted by educators. Unfortunately there is nothing about his principles that can be assimilated by either progressives or traditionalists; they are revolutionary and will call for a fundamental revision of hypotheses; up to date educators have avoided the responsibility that either acceptance or rejection would entail, and have ignored them. And yet to all except incurable Panglosses who insist that everything is currently being done for the best, a theory which claims to account for educational failures as well as successes, deserves the most careful examination.

Never before in history has so much attention been paid to the child—his posture, his diet, his social adjustments, his spiritual development. He is placed under the care of experts from the moment of birth. Teachers have been trained as never before and so have parents, and public and private money has been lavishly spent. Almost everything that could be done to a child or for a child has been done. The result should be healthier, less nervous, and better adjusted children than the country or the world has known; and yet not even the most enthusiastic supporter of modern education would claim that this is so.

All education today, whether traditional or progressive, is based on the principle that the first duty of the educator is to find out what is right for the pupil to do and then teach him how to do it. The underlying assumption here is that all children are in possession of a sensory appreciation that will enable them to learn any new specialized activity without in any way upsetting their total pattern of activity. The assumption, however, is false. It is only necessary to watch a child learning such a skill as writing (or reading) to realize that something is wrong. To consider it a success if one has taught a child to write quickly and legibly without taking into consideration other deep-seated and bad nervous habits that have developed is as if one were to practise double-entry bookkeeping by putting down only the credit items. For every credit item accruing to the various systems in vogue there is a debit, for which, however, an entry is seldom made.

One of the most useful devices employed in the old-fashioned schools was competition. It is now frowned upon and used as sparingly as possible, with the result that a school term is a glorified caucus race ending with prizes for everyone. Alexander has solved the problem by providing the student competition with himself—in a sense that is quite unique.

On change

In the Alexander work the one thing essential for progress is for the pupil to accept responsibility for his own shortcomings. It is this initial step that is the most difficult to make, but once it has been made the path becomes easy; for the pupil has in effect said, "The blame for my troubles is my own, since it is something I myself am doing that interferes with my best development; however, I now know the means for learning what those things are and for stopping them." Other scientific projects for human betterment do not make this demand. They allow the individual to place the blame outside him-self. Thus they offer a feeling of comfort and security, but no cure.

The great trouble with the Alexander work, from the ordinary point of view, is that it demands a total change. Doctors and reform-ers, on the other hand, let the individual pick out that part of him-self he will have changed and improved—his vision, or his stomach, or his temper, or his memory. To make the desired change he may be asked to give up certain habits to which he is attached, but the rest of his life is his own to do with as he pleases. Unfortunately, by this method, no real improvement is possible.

For the ordinary person, habit-pleasures like smoking are not real pleasures at all but temporary ways of alleviating pain or discom-fort or nervousness. The habit itself, when indulged, produces a new discomfort or pain, but it produces discomfort also when it is not indulged. A healthy person should be able on any occasion to choose between two pleasures, the pleasure of smoking or the pleasure of not smoking, and get satisfaction out of either choice.

In my experience, suffering and being conscious of it is a neces-sary condition for fundamental change—small gradual changes take place almost automatically. Salvation then lies in the understanding and acceptance of change.

Refusal to accept change is paradoxical because you are chang-ing anyway—it is not a question of "change *vs.* no change" but of changing for the better instead of for the worse.

The important stage is the recognition that something is wrong and that you can stop contributing to it and thus change the direc-tion of the process.

On self-responsibility

Science has undoubtedly progressed in the last 2,000 years but from one point of view the average man is no better off than he was. He is still dependent upon "experts"—now perhaps more than ever. He has no means in himself for determining the nature of his ailments and deciding on a procedure that will remedy the situation. And as in the past, one "expert" will recommend one thing and another something quite different, and the victim has no way of choosing between them.

An advantage Alexander teachers have over other teachers or physicians is that all the facts needed for their diagnosis are to be found in the activity of the pupil as manifested in lessons. There is no need to ask impertinent questions or to give scientific value to the replies.

Be your own expert: no one else can really give you expert advice about yourself, but you can become your own expert. This, however, demands self-study and responsibility.

On relaxation

Though a feeling of relaxation is sometimes reported by subjects to whom the Alexander Technique has been demonstrated, relaxation is not a goal of the teaching, nor is it the means by which change comes about. In the Technique tension is not treated as a something bad to be got rid of but as a form of energy to be redirected and redistributed. Pupils sometimes start lessons with the belief that learning the Technique will somehow be easier and quicker if they can do something, think something or take something that will relax them first: the contrary is the case. Other things being equal, a person who is overly tense is much easier to teach than one who is overly relaxed. "An empty sack cannot stand alone."

After a first lesson people frequently report that they feel relaxed. Undoubtedly their trunks and limbs have been lengthened and muscles have been lengthened, producing a feeling of pleasant relaxation. If the pupil associates this feeling with the Technique he may try later on to recapture it by "relaxing" in the way he understands by "relaxing," which to most people means being heavy.

The test for relaxation in Jacobson et al. is to pick up a person's arm and then let go of it: if it falls immediately it is relaxed. This is not the case in the Alexander Technique; the arm should fall or not fall just as the subject chooses; the anti-gravity response in arm muscles have been activated by the movement and the tonus thus created should persist as long as it serves a purpose—(not *that* it falls but *how* it falls is significant).

On ethics

[Some] are unwilling to admit that the Alexander principle offers any help for the solution of ethical problems. And others have even said that it might make a wicked man more wicked by adding to his efficiency. Isn't the answer that the Technique, by making you more aware of underlying conflicts, makes it more difficult to accept an unrealistic solution for them? As you go on in the work you are forced to see yourself more nearly as you are.

It is a commonplace that most wrong acts would be avoided if their consequences were immediately apparent. It is seldom, however, that punishment directly follows the crime. The man who eats poison, to be sure, is punished for it at once, but the evil effects of most foods and drugs are not obvious at the start. One great benefit of the Alexander work is that it makes the consequences of an action more obvious to the subject by increasing his awareness. For example, a slump is admittedly harmful, but it is only indirectly that the bad effects (e.g. indigestion, backache, etc.) are apparent to the subject. To one trained in the Alexander Technique, however, a slump feels wrong from the start.

NOTES

The Alexander Technique helps in the field of perception by expanding and/or organizing the field so that it has a constant framework, i.e., the self.

* * *

There is nothing wrong with either exercise or relaxation—the question is, is it mindless or intelligent?

* * *

Inhibition is the conscious avoidance of response patterns which interfere with the automatic functioning of the primary control.

* * *

In the ordinary person habit controls and directs thought— Alexander's technique reverses this.

* * *

Some people are perfectly willing to keep their disabilities if they can blame something or someone else for them.

* * *

If "habitual" is substituted for "wrong" and "experimental" for "right", a pupil can make much faster progress. What you are studying to obtain is a better understanding of your habitual responses as a preliminary to constructive change.

* * *

Inhibition is more than stopping and "saying 'no'." It is quite possible to stop, delay your response and then go ahead and do what you have already done before—it means not only not responding in the old way but permitting a new response to take place. The mechanism which makes the transition possible is the facilitation of the lengthening response which is pleasurable in itself and is reinforcing. Inhibition has to be rewarding if unlearning is to take place

* * *

Once you have learned the Technique it doesn't cost you anything to practice it and benefit from it—either in money or time.

* * *

The Technique does two things simultaneously—it displays the prison house of habit in which the individual is enclosed and gives him the combination of the lock.

* * *

A. R. said one day, "The trouble with most pupils is that they think they are taking lessons in order to learn something, whereas they should be taking them to unlearn."

* * *

Hilgard et al. in *Introduction to Psychology* (Harcourt, 1971, pp. 173–74) lists eight characteristics of hypnotizability. For each of them the Alexander Technique would produce almost the opposite behavior.

* * *

F. M. Alexander's discovery leads to a concept—an operational concept—that embraces both the conscious and the subconscious so that the current dichotomy ceases to have meaning.

* * *

The Alexander Technique is a method for improving motor performances by integrating the voluntary and reflex components of a movement in such way that the voluntary does not interfere with the reflex and the reflex facilitates the voluntary.

It is a method for playing the violin or looking through a microscope without getting a stiff neck—for playing the piano or sewing without low back pain—for studying or listening to a lecture without mind wandering. While allowing the individual to take advantage of specific learning techniques it leaves him free to change behaviour patterns which for any reason have become undesirable.

* * *

Glossary

Adductor muscles —Muscles which draw toward the medial plane, for example the muscles on the inside of the legs or arms.

Adjusted movement—A movement in which the subject is guided into the starting position by an experimenter skilled in teaching the Alexander Technique, but not guided during the movement itself.

Biofeedback —A configuration of apparatus for recording biological signals (from the brain, heart, muscles, etc.) and displaying them as feedback to a subject, enabling the subject to achieve voluntary control over physiological functions.

Conscious control—Alexander's term for the constructive guidance which an individual can apply, not just to the movement of specific muscles but to all spheres of mental and physical activity.

Curative measures —Those measures which treat specific symptoms or problems but ignore the influence of faulty use upon functioning when dealing with the disorder.

Direction; orders —The process of projecting messages from the brain to the mechanisms and of conducting energy for the use of these mechanisms. Orders commonly refer to the messages used in teaching the Alexander Technique. For example, a student is asked to order the neck to relax, to order the head forward and up, to lengthen and widen the back.

Electromyography—A polygraph technique for recording the electrical activity of muscles.

End-gaining—An orientation toward an end to be achieved, which distracts the person from the steps (means-whereby) needed to achieve the end. An end-gaining orientation prevents the application of conscious control and may lead to uncoordinated use.

Guided movement —A movement during which an experimenter skilled in teaching the Alexander Technique maintains light contact with his hands to prevent postural sets in the subject.

Habit—An acquired predisposition to respond to a certain class of stimuli with a certain mode of response.

Inhibition —In general, any suspension of activity or temporary withholding of a response. In Alexander's usage, inhibition releases, rather than represses, spontaneity by suspending habitual responses to stimuli long enough for intelligent guidance and reasoning to intervene. Alexander saw this ability to inhibit automatic responses to stimuli, and to allow reason to intervene before making responses, as "man's supreme inheritance."

Intelligence—The ability to use the intellectual faculties (learning, memory, etc.) to respond adaptively to the environment.

Jacobson, Edmund —The originator of a system of deep muscle relaxation described in his books *Progressive Relaxation* and *You Must Relax.*

Kinaesthesia —A general term for the sensations (of tension, weight, position) from muscles, tendons and joints and from the gravity receptors in the inner ear. Kinaesthesia supplies information about the state of the body as it interacts with an environment.

Ligamentum nuchae —A fibrous structure in the back of the neck connecting the occiput to the cervical spines. According to Campbell (1966) this structure plays an important rôle in counterbalancing the weight of the head.

Magnitude estimation—A psycho-physical scaling technique in which subjects assign numerical values to stimuli, using either units of their own choosing or units previously defined by the presentation of a stimulus of a standard magnitude.

Means-whereby —The coordinated series of intermediate steps which must be accomplished in order to attain an end. The means-whereby principle is the recognition in practice that these intermediate steps are important as ends in themselves, and that the most important step at any time is the *next* one. Application of the means-whereby principle involves awareness of the conditions present, a reasoned consideration of their causes, inhibition of habitual or end-gaining responses to these conditions, and consciously guided performance of the indirect series of steps required to gain the end.

Mensendieck, Bess—The originator of a system of postural training and the author of *Look Better, Feel Better: The World Renowned Mensendieck System of Functional Movements.*

Orders —see Direction.

Postural set —A preparation for movement.

Posture —The attitude of the body at any specific time.

Preventive measures —All attempts to prevent disorder and disease based on the assumption that the individual may take responsibility for his health by preventing faulty use and functioning.

Primary control—F. M. Alexander's discovery that a dynamic relationship of the head and the neck promotes maximal lengthening of the body and facilitates movement throughout the body. Physiologically it is the stimulus (head–neck relation) which serves to activate the anti-gravity reflexes. Anatomically it is a dynamic balance of the forces acting on the head and spine such that the centre of gravity of the head moves forward and the weight of the head is counterbalanced by increased tension in the *Ligamentum nuchae.*

Reflex —A relatively simple response which is rapidly and automatically elicited by a specific stimulus. Reflexive behaviour is unlearned and is controlled by direct connections in the nervous system between receptors and effectors.

Sensory appreciation —Activity associated with the perception of a stimulus which determines how an individual will respond to the stimulus. Because of the differences in sensory appreciation the same objective stimulus may result in different experiences and lead to different emotions, movements or opinions.

Set—A state of readiness to respond with a particular class of behaviour. Set depends upon the activity in the brain which narrows the range of possible responses.

Subconscious control —Control of functioning not mediated by the volition of the subject—as in hypnotic suggestion, etc.

Tone —The mechanical tension in a muscle. The general tone of a muscle is determined by both the passive elasticity of the muscular and fibrous tissues and by neuromuscular activity. Completely relaxed muscles may still have tone even without neuromuscular activity because of the way they are stretched on the skeletal frame. In response to a stronger stretch stimulus, as in postural muscles supporting the weight of the body, there will be continuous evoked neuromuscular activity. Tonic activity has the connotation of relatively long-lasting or enduring activity of a nerve or muscle.

Use —In the narrower sense, use describes posture as it changes over time. You have poor posture at a given time because of the poor way you use your body. In the broader sense, use describes the total pattern of behaviour in the ongoing present. Alexander emphasized that by use he did not mean use of specific parts, but use of all parts of the organism acting in concert.

Select Bibliography

Alexander, F. M. *Conscious Control*, London: Methuen & Co., 1912. (incorporated into 1918 edition of *Man's Supreme Inheritance*)

——*Constructive Conscious Control of the Individual*, London: Methuen & Co., 1924.

——*Man's Supreme Inheritance*, New York: D.R. Reynolds, 1910. 2nd ed. New York: Dutton, 1918.

——"Re-education of the Kinesthetic Systems (Sensory Appreciation of Muscular Movement) Concerned with the Development of Robust Physical Well-Being" (pamphlet), London, 1908. Reprinted in *Man's Supreme Inheritance*, 1st ed. (Alexander, 1910), pp. 185-89.

——*The Resurrection of the Body: The Essential Writings of F. Matthias Alexander, Selected and Introduced by Edward Maisel*, New York: Dell Publishing Company, 1974.

——"The Theory and Practice of a New Method of Respiratory Reeducation," London: Balliere & Co., 1907. Reprinted in *Man's Supreme Inheritance*, 4th ed., pp. 188–205.

——*The Universal Constant in Living*, New York: Dutton, 1941.

——*The Use of the Self*, New York: Dutton, 1932.

——"Why We Breathe Incorrectly," (pamphlet), London, 1909.

Barlow, W. "The Alexander Libel Action," *Lancet*, 1950, 259(2): 26–30.

——*The Alexander Principle*, London: Victor Gollancz, 1973.

——"Anxiety and Muscle Tension," *British Journal of Physical Medicine*, 1947, 10, 81–87.

Barlow, W. (ed.) *Knowing How to Stop*, London: Chaterson, 1946.

——"Postural homeostasis," *Annals of Physical Medicine*, July 1952, 1, 77–89.

——"Posture and the resting state," *Annals of Medicine*, 1954, 2, (No. 4).

Barlow, W. and Morrison, D. (Letter 1), *British Medical Journal*, February 4, 1950.

Bourne, R. ("R.B.") "Making over the Body," *New Republic*, XV, May 4, 1918, pp. 28–29.

——"Other Messiahs ", *New Republic*, XV, May 25, 1918, p. 117.

Campbell, B. G, *Human Evolution*, Chicago: Aldine Publishing Co., 1966, p. 99 (fig. 4.13)

Coaker, N. "A review of the case of Alexander v. Cluver, Jokl & Clark," *The Commercial Law Reporter*, November, 1949, 650–62.

Coghill, G. E. *Anatomy and the Problem of Behaviour*, London lecture, 1929.

——"Appreciation: The Educational Methods of F. Matthias Alexander," in *The Universal Constant in Living* (Alexander, 1941), pp. xxi–xxviii.

DePuky, P. "The Physiological Oscillation of the Length of the Body," *Acta Orthop. Scandanavica*, 1935, 6, 338–47.

Dewey, J. *Art as Experience*, New York: G. P. Putnam & Sons, 1934.

——*Experience and Education*, New York: Macmillan, 1938. (New York: Macmillan, 1959)

——*Experience and Nature*, New York: W.W. Norton & Co., 1929.

——*How We Think*, Rev. ed. Boston: D.C. Heath & Co., 1933.

——*Human Nature and Conduct*, New York: Modern Library, 1930.

——The Quest for Certainty, New York: G.P. Putnam's Sons, 1939.

——"Reply to a reviewer," *New Republic*, 1918, 15:55.

——"A Sick World," *New Republic*, XXXIII, January 24, 1923.

——"The Theory of Valuation," *International Encyclopedia of Unified Science*, Chicago: 1939 (published separately).

Douglas, M. "Reorientation of the Viewpoint upon the Study of Anatomy," in *The Universal Constant in Living*, Alexander, 1941.

Duchenne, G. B. *Physiologie des mouvements*. (Orig. pub. 1867) (*Physiology of Motion*, trans. by E. B. Kaplan) Phila: W. B. Saunders, 1959.

Dykhuizen, C. *The Life and Mind of John Dewey*, Carbondale: Southern Illinois University Press, 1973.

Eastman, Max. *Heroes I Have Known*, Ch. 12 "The Hero as Teacher," pp. 275–321, New York: Simon & Schuster, 1942. (Originally published in the *Atlantic Monthly*, 1941, 168, 683.)

Griffith, I. G. "The F. Matthias Alexander Technique and its relation to education," in *Knowing How to Stop* (Barlow, ed., 1946).

Herrick, C. J. *George Ellett Coghill*, Chicago: U. of Chicago Press, 1949.

Hodge, R.M. "What is Man's Supreme Inheritance," *New York Times Book Review*, May 5, 1918.

Huxley, A. "Education of an Amphibian," in *Tomorrow and Tomorrow and Tomorrow*, New York: Harper & Row, 1952.

——*Ends and Means*, New York: Harper & Brothers, 1937.

——"End-gaining and means-whereby," *The Saturday Review of Literature*, October 25, 1941.

——*Eyeless in Gaza*, New York: Harper & Row, 1936.

——*The Letters of Aldous Huxley*, edited by Grover Smith, New York: Harper & Row, 1970.
——"What a Piece of Work is a Man," M.I.T. Lectures, 1960.
Jokl, Ernst. "Quackery versus Physical Education," editorial in *Volkskragte* (*Manpower*), March 1944, 2, 2–45.
Jones, F. P. "Finding the Whole Person" (Review), *Providence Sunday Journal,* January 11, 1942.
——"The Work of F. M. Alexander as an Introduction to Dewey's Philosophy of Education," *School and Society,* January 2, 1943, 1–4.
——"The role of classics in the emancipation of women," *Classical Journal,* 1944, Vol. 39, 326–42.
——"The influence of postural set on pattern movement in man," *International Journal of Neurology,* 1963, 4, 60–71.
——"Die kinästhetische Wahrnemung von Haltung und Bewegung," in *Eutonie,* Karl F. Haug Verlag, Ulm/Donau, 1964, 100–125.
——"Method for changing stereotyped response patterns by the inhibition of certain postural sets," *Psychological Review,* 1965, 72, 196–214.
——"An experimental study of the Alexander Technique," *Stud. Med.* (Copenhagen), April 1971, Vol. 35, No. 2.
——"Voice production as a function of head balance in singers," *Journal of Psychology,* 1972, 82, 209–15.
Jones, F. P. and Gilley, P. F. M., Jr. "Head balance and sitting posture: an X-ray analysis," *Journal of Psychology,* 1960, 49, 289–93.
Jones, F. P., Gray, F. E., Hanson, J. A. and O'Connell, D. N. "An experimental study of the effect of head balance on patterns of posture and movement in man," *Journal of Psychology,* 1959, 47, 247–58.
Jones, F. P. and Hanson, J. A. "Time-space pattern in a gross body movement," *Perceptual and Motor Skills,* 1961, 12, 35–41.
——"Note on the persistence of pattern in a gross body movement," *Perceptual and Motor Skills,* 1962, 14, 230.
——"Postural set and overt movement: a force-platform analysis," *Perceptual and Motor Skills,* 1970, 30, 699–702.
Jones, F.P., Hanson, J.A. and Gray, F. E. "Head balance and sitting posture II: the role of the sternomastoid muscle." *Journal of Psychology,* 1961, 52, 363–67.
——"Startle as a paradigm of malposture," *Perceptual and Motor Skills,* 1964, 19, 21–22.
Jones, F. P., Hanson, J. A., Miller, J. K., and Bossom, J. "Quantitative analysis of abnormal movement: the sit-to-stand pattern," *American Journal of Physical Medicine,* 1963, 42, 208-18.

Jones, F. P. and Kennedy, J. L. "An electromyographic technique for recording the startle pattern," *Journal of Psychology*, 1951, 32, 63–68.

Jones, F. P. and Narva, M. "Interrupted light photography to record the effect of changes in the poise of the head upon patterns of movement and posture in man," *Journal of Psychology*, 1955, 40, 124–31.

Jones, F. P. and O'Connell, D. N. "Applications of multiple-image photography in the time–motion analysis of human movement," *Photographic Science and Technique*, 1956, Ser. II (3), 11–14.

——"Stereo plus electronic flash record human movements," *Industrial Psychology*, 1957, 36–39.

——"Color coding of multiple-image photography," *Science*, May, 1958, 127, 1119.

——"Posture as a function of time," *Journal of Psychology*, 1958, 46, 287–94.

Jones, F. P., O'Connell, D. N., and Hanson, J. A. "Color-coded multiple image photography for studying related rates of movement," *Journal of Psychology*, 1958, 45, 247–51.

Jones, H. R. "Postural Responses of Third Grade Children in Reading and Writing," Master's Thesis, Tufts University, August, 1965.

Kallen, H. M. "Conscious Control of the Body," *Dial*, June 6, 1918, pp. 533–34.

Lamont, C. *Dialogue on John Dewey*, New York: Horizon Press, 1959.

Lee, G. S. *Invisible Exercise: Seven Studies in Self-Command With Practical Suggestions and Drills*, New York: Dutton, 1922.

Ludovici, A. M. *Health and Education through Self-Mastery*, London: Watts & Co., 1933.

——*The Truth about Childbirth*, London: Kegan Paul & Co., 1937.

McCormack, E. D. "Frederick Matthias Alexander and John Dewey: A Neglected influence," Doctoral dissertation, University of Toronto, 1958.

Macdonald, P. "Instinct and Functioning in Health and Disease," *British Medical Journal*, 1926, 2, 1221–23. Reprinted in *Knowing How to Stop* (Barlow, ed., 1946).

Magnus, R. "Animal Posture," *Proceedings of the Royal Society of London*, 1925, 98 (Ser. B), 339–53.

——*Körperstelling*, Berlin: Springer, 1924. (*Body Posture*, ed. by A. Van Harreveld, unknown publisher and date, but later than 1974. Available from U. S. Department of Commerce, Springfield, Virginia).

——"Physiology of Posture," *Lancet*, 1926, 211, 531–36; 585–88.

——"The Physiological *a priori*," Lane lectures on experimental pharmacology and medicine: III, Stanford University Publications, 1930 (Series V 2, No. 3), 331–37.

March, M. (Arthur F. Busch) "A New Way of Life: An Introduction to the Work of F. Matthias Alexander" (pamphlet), London: 1946.

Morgan, L. *Inside Yourself*, London: Hutchinson, 1954.

Murdoch, A. "The Function of the Sub-Occipital Muscles: The Key to Posture, Use, and Functioning," reprinted in *The Universal Constant in Living*, (Alexander, 1941).

O'Leary, J. P. "A strain-gauge force platform for studying human movement," *Perceptual and Motor Skills*, 1970, 30, 698.

Robinson, J. H. "The Philosopher's Stone," *Atlantic Monthly*, February, 1919, pp. 474–81.

Shaw, B. "Preface to London Music in 1888–89," Reprinted in *Shaw on Music: A Selection from the Music Criticism of Bernard Shaw*, ed. by Eric Bentley, pp. 1–32, New York: Doubleday, 1955.

Sherrington, C. S. *The Integrative Action of the Nervous System*, New Haven: Yale University Press, 1906.

——*The Endeavor of Jean Fernel*, London: Cambridge University Press, 1946.

Stein, L. *Journey into the Self*, New York: Crown Publishers, 1950.

Tasker, I. "An unrecognized need in education," *Journal of Science*, (South African Association for the Advancement of Science) July, 1942.

Tinbergen, N. "Ethology and Stress Diseases," *Science*, 1974, 185: 20–27.

Westfeldt, L. F. *Matthias Alexander: The Man and His Work*, Westport, Conn.: Associated Booksellers, 1964.

Index

Page reference in italics refer to an entry in the glossary.